Health Ethics Guide

THIRD EDITION

2012

First Printing – September 2012

Nihil obstat: The *Health Ethics Guide* was approved by the Permanent
Council of the Canadian Conference of Catholic Bishops in May 2012.

Photo credits – Front cover: iStockphoto; page 18: St. Joseph's Health
Centre, Guelph; pages 54 and 68: Covenant Health, Edmonton; back cover:
photo and sculpture of *The Good Samaritan* by Fr. Herman Falke, Ottawa.

Library and Archives Canada Cataloguing in Publication

Health ethics guide.

Includes index.
ISBN 978-0-920705-43-8

1. Medical ethics. 2. Medicine--Religious aspects--Catholic Church.
3. Catholic health facilities. 4. Christian ethics--Catholic authors.
I. Catholic Health Alliance of Canada

R725.56.C38 2012   174.2   C2010-901351-4

Published by the Catholic Health Alliance of Canada
Annex C, Saint-Vincent Hospital
60 Cambridge Street North, Ottawa, ON K1R 7A5
Telephone: 613-562-6262 ext. 2164
www.chac.ca

Distributed by: Novalis
To order copies go to: www.novalis.ca
E-mail: books@novalis.ca
NOVALIS Tel: 1-800-387-7164 (toll-free Canada and US only)
Fax: 1-800-204-4140

Table of Contents

Acknowledgements

This third edition of the *Health Ethics Guide* is based on the work of an extremely large number of people who volunteered their time and expertise to bring to fruition this communal reflection on health ethics in the Catholic tradition. Naming everyone would be a difficult task. However, some of that number who were most involved should be recognized.

The process was ably coordinated and directed throughout by James Roche.

The Steering Committee members who initiated the review process in 2007 were Rev. Michael Prieur, James Roche, Pat Murphy, Gordon Self, Moira McQueen and Ashley Carlson.

The Core Group members from 2007 to 2010 with overall responsibility for the subcommittees for each chapter and for the final guide were Rev. Michael Prieur (Chairperson), Archbishop Bertrand Blanchet, Eoin Connolly, Hazel Markwell, Sr. Nuala Kenny, Pat Murphy, James Roche, Gordon Self, Bishop Noël Simard, Michael Coughlin (Editor) and Greg Humbert (layout and design). In addition, Richard Fraser, QC, provided a legal review of the guide.

We are also grateful to Rev. Francis Morrisey OMI and Rev. Jack Gallagher CSB for their assistance during the process leading to the granting of the *nihil obstat* by the Canadian Conference of Catholic Bishops.

At the beginning of the process, a large group of reviewers provided essential feedback on the adequacy of the 2000 *Health Ethics Guide,* along with suggestions for revision. Subsequently,

Core Group members chaired subcommittees for each chapter; each subcommittee included a number of additional members who reviewed the state of the field covered in each chapter and articulated the additions and revisions to be incorporated. This group provided invaluable input from a wide range of professionals, Canadian and international, with experience in health care, ethics and theology.

This additional group of volunteer reviewers and subcommittee members included Rev. Robert Allore SJ, Sr. Anne Anderson CSJ, Andrew Baker, Carolyn Baker, Jean Bartkowiak, Sandra Bazley, Rev. Walter Black MSC, Barry Brown, Bridget Campion, Tom Corbett, John Dossetor, Bishop Brian Dunn, Marguerite Evans, Len Evenson, Rory Fisher, Michael George, Joseph Gilbert, Robert Gordon, Rev. Richard Gula SS, Michael Hadskis, Ron Hamel, Laurie Hardingham, Gerry Heeley, John Heng, Melody Isinger, Sr. Joan Kalchbrenner RHSJ, Rev. Roger Keeler, Michael Keim, Jennifer Leddy, Rene Leiva, David Levangie, Margaret Love, Abbyann Lynch, Tom Maddix CSC, Ron Marr, Susan McClement, Don McDermott, Moira McQueen, Rev. Mark Miller CSsR, Patricia Murphy, Cliff Nordal, Rev. Kevin O'Rourke OP, Pat Pocock, Zinia Pritchard, Carol Taylor, Rev. John Perry SJ, Larry Reynolds, Sr. Mary Rowell CSJ, Giles Scofield, Rev. Myles Sheehan SJ, Margaret Somerville, Daniel Sulmasy OFM, Carol Taylor, Rev. Leo Walsh CSB, Helen Watt and George Webster. Reviews were also received from various ethics committees: Ethics Committee, Covenant Health, Edmonton; Ethics Committee, St. Joseph's Health Care, London; Ethics Council, St. Boniface General Hospital, Winnipeg; and Ethics Committee, St. Joseph's Residence, Winnipeg.

Preamble

The 1991 *Health Care Ethics Guide* published by the Catholic Health Association of Canada stated that the guide should be examined and revised at regular intervals as newer insights occur, and in order to respond better to the ethical issues of the day. The subsequent *Health Ethics Guide* published in 2000 was such a revision. It included an increased focus on health care in the community and on the widening social dimensions of health care such as health promotion and disease prevention, social services, acute care, long-term care, chronic care rehabilitation and home care. This current revision of the *Health Ethics Guide* is again meant to provide guidance around new advances in science and medicine. Moreover, it seeks to more firmly ground the guide in the Gospel message of Jesus as exemplified in the parable of the Good Samaritan, which serves as a model of how to respond to one's neighbour in need. In addition, this revision of the *Health Ethics Guide* incorporates a more fully articulated vision of the social nature of health care along with the values and principles that are embedded in the parable of the Good Samaritan.

The *Health Ethics Guide* is intended to assist a number of different audiences. It is written with the recognition that many staff and even board members and administrators today are less familiar with the Catholic tradition and the legacy of Catholic health care than formerly.

Most specifically, the *Health Ethics Guide* outlines the moral obligations for the sponsors/owners, boards, members of ethics committees and personnel of Catholic health and social service organizations. For Catholics working in health and social service organizations that are not Catholic sponsored, the *Health Ethics Guide* provides valuable assistance. For people who work in Catholic health and social service organizations, regardless of whether they are members of the Catholic faith tradition, the *Health Ethics Guide* presents Catholic teaching and outlines the values that are to be respected by those who work within the organization. Finally, the *Health Ethics Guide* can be used by persons receiving care, their families and anyone who seeks a framework to structure and articulate their own decision making. It also informs them about what to expect from care providers who function according to such a vision of care.

Such a guide can provide a perspective and a general direction. It does not substitute for the direction and teaching of Church authorities or for organizational responsibilities or for the need to follow an informed conscience.

The *Health Ethics Guide* serves to guide the development of local protocols. The *nihil obstat* of the Permanent Council of the Canadian Conference of Catholic Bishops does not serve as a substitute for the authority of the diocesan bishop, but aims to support it. Local protocols will defer to the judgement of the diocesan bishop when there is a question of faith or morals.

The *Health Ethics Guide* complements other initiatives in the Church's healing ministry, such as spiritual and religious care, organizational mission and values integration, ethics committees and centres, and parish-based ministry and nursing, through which caregivers are becoming more aware of the broader aspects of their healing ministry.

Most of the chapters are composed of two parts: introductory comments identifying the values that underlie the treatment of issues discussed in the chapter, and articles that serve as formulations of contemporary Catholic teaching on how these values are to be applied in particular circumstances.

Although the guide focuses on ethical issues, many of them have legal ramifications. Where needed, readers are encouraged to refer to the appropriate provincial, territorial and federal legislation.

Introduction

LOVING COMPASSION AND THE HEALING RELATIONSHIP: THE CONTEXT OF ETHICAL REFLECTION

The Catholic Health Alliance of Canada begins this *Health Ethics Guide* with a reflection on the Gospel and the ongoing healing mission of Jesus Christ.

When Jesus heals a leper or proclaims the parable of the Good Samaritan, it is an obvious sign of his compassion for those in suffering. But even more it points to the new life of the Kingdom: the total and permanent healing of the human person in all [the person's] dimensions and relationships. Jesus' healing Word of power reaches the whole person.[1]

Mindful that the parable of the Good Samaritan is one of the foundational stories of Catholic health care,[2] we begin this guide by reflecting upon, identifying with and acting upon the lessons contained within this parable given to us by Christ Himself.

But the man was anxious to justify himself and said to Jesus, "And who is my neighbour?" Jesus replied, "A man was once on his way down from Jerusalem to Jericho and fell into the hands of brigands; they took all he had,

---

1. Canadian Conference of Catholic Bishops, *New Hope in Christ: A Pastoral Message on Sickness and Healing*, 1983, p. 10, n. 11.

2. G. Arbuckle, "Retelling 'The Good Samaritan': Jesus' parable is the founding story of Catholic health care". *Health Progress* (July–August 2007) 88(4):20-24.

*beat him and then made off, leaving him half dead.
Now a priest happened to be travelling down the same
road but when he saw the man, he passed by on the
other side. In the same way a Levite who came to the
same place saw him, and passed by on the other side.
But a Samaritan traveller who came upon him was
moved with compassion when he saw him. He went up
and bandaged his wounds, pouring oil and wine on
them. He then lifted him onto his own mount, carried
him to the inn and looked after him. Next day, he took
out two denarii and handed them to the innkeeper.
'Look after him,' he said, 'and on my way back I will
make good any extra expense you have.' Which of these
three, do you think, proved himself a neighbour to the
man who fell into the brigands' hands?" "The one who
took pity on him," he replied. Jesus said to him, "Go
and do the same yourself."* (Luke 10:29-37)[3]

Jesus' paradigm parable of the Good Samaritan focuses us on the
centrality of loving compassion and the relationship of healing.
The story has lessons for us today for every facet of health care
in all the locations in which we serve: community health centre,
social service agency, hospital, long-term care facility, residential
home, or people's own homes. First and foremost, Jesus sets the
response of care firmly within the call of charity. Charity, the
love of Christ, is at the heart of each individual's response and
ought to be the foundation of institutional and organizational
response. Jesus Himself, in His preaching and teaching, gives us
a model of loving service. Jesus also identifies Himself with the

---

3. *The New Testament of the Jerusalem Bible* (Reader's Edition), Doubleday
   & Company Inc. Garden City, NY, 1969.

sick and the needy, making it very clear that responding to the sick and suffering is responding to Jesus. All those who work in Catholic health care, then, are called to manifest the loving compassion of Christ today and to serve the Lord in those who suffer. While we are about the business of health care in the twenty-first century, we are reminded that serving those in need is far more than business. It is our ongoing participation in the healing ministry of Jesus Christ.

Each element in this parable challenges us to look at our own experience and our compassionate response to those in need of health care. The Good Samaritan challenges Catholic health and social services explicitly to respect dignity, foster trust in care and promote just health systems.

In the following reflections, the questions raised by the parable provide a context within which we invite the reader to engage this third edition of the *Health Ethics Guide*. It is precisely these questions that require an authentic response in the face of the many complex ethical questions arising in the delivery of health and social services today. The *Health Ethics Guide* sets out to provide clear direction to support health and social service personnel in responding to these questions within a consistent ethical framework.

The Call to Respect Dignity

A man with an obvious severe health need has been beaten half to death. He needs health care urgently. As a victim of violence he also has a need for compassion and respectful care (inner healing).

Who are the persons in need of urgent care today? What are the ways in which we, individually and collectively, are blind to or avoid the obvious need of some persons?

Despite the urgency of the situation, no one is responding to his need. The formal authorities who might be expected to respond because of their positions as priest and Levite actually go out of their way to pass him by. They get on with the busyness of their lives in a kind of moral blindness to the need that is right before them.

How does Catholic health care respond to new and emerging needs and changing circumstances? What kind of courage does it require to recognize and respond to both obvious physical need and the deeper needs for restoration of a sense of dignity and inner healing? What are the consequences for overworked caregivers who try to go the extra distance in responding to the spiritual and emotional needs of the sick and injured? Are there forms of 'violence' perpetrated by our own care giving and professional practices?

Are we so caught up in the urgency and stress of our usual responses to the many needs of those we serve today that we lose the opportunity to be truly compassionate for the persons and in the places that need it most?

Persons are created to be in relationships that nurture and define them. The Catholic tradition sees this encounter between persons as a privileged place for supporting their intrinsic human dignity.

• All care is to be marked by attention to the good of the person. Those in need of care should always be welcomed as persons with whom we are willing to be in relationship. Respect is given to the communal aspects of the person's identity, whether cultural, religious, or linguistic.

- Healing occurs best when people experience that they belong to communities of compassion. Faith communities have a special role in nurturing people and in attending to the spiritual/religious dimensions of care.
- Prejudice of any kind represents a fundamental denial of our commitment to the Gospel message.
- Health and social service organizations must respect the dignity of personnel in the same way that personnel are expected to respect the dignity of those in their care.

The Call to Foster Trust in Care

Unexpectedly, in the parable, it is a Samaritan, one who was considered by the orthodox and powerful of the time as both heretic and social inferior, who is "moved with compassion" for the injured man. A sense of interconnectedness (of being "neighbour") and of mutual vulnerability opens up as the Samaritan leaves the safety of his mount to come down to the level of the injured man, and the injured man accepts care from a social outcast.

What are the challenges to compassionate care in our time? Do our institutions and organizations recognize the mutual vulnerability inherent in truly compassionate care? What policies and practices do we engage in to foster trust in the people we care for? How do we support caregivers moved by compassion who challenge the routine and accepted? How much of the challenge is created by our organization of care? How much by pressures of time and money? How does the multi-cultural and multi-ethnic landscape of modern health care present challenges for patients and health care providers alike?

The compassion demonstrated here is not some vague feeling of being sorry for or of feeling empathy but a robust virtue of "suffering with" that demands a courageous and generous response of care. The Samaritan tends to the wounds with his own hands. He uses his own precious resources of wine and oil for care. There is a real cost to compassion in the story.

As health systems are pressured to respond to issues of access and expectation, how do we model solidarity in our care for the sick? What price are we willing to pay as individuals and organizations to ensure just and compassionate care?

The Catholic tradition holds that healing is best effected in an atmosphere of trust.

- The compassion and trust that have been characteristic of health and social service organizations protect society against a growing depersonalization.

- Persons in need of care need to feel that they can trust health care providers to act in their best interests with respect and with the highest regard for quality and safety.

- Organizations need to embody a trust rooted in dialogue and mutual respect.

- Attentiveness to the well-being of health care workers is an essential component of trust; this requires a commitment to foster respect for the unique contribution of each, co-responsibility, accountability, and communication.

- Those in positions of leadership must recognize that their ministry is, first of all, a ministry of loving service and stewardship. A commitment to share authority and power and to encourage participative decision making, planning and policy formation is essential to developing an environment of trust in organizations and systems.

The Call to Promote Justice

The Samaritan does not simply respond to the immediate need. He recognizes the long-term need for care, support and rehabilitation that the injured man requires. He lifts him up onto his own mount and takes him to an inn where the man can be cared for during his long recovery. Finding and arranging for this long-term care is not easy.

How attentive are we at every level of Catholic health care to issues in the full continuum of health care needs from disease prevention and health promotion to long-term care, rehabilitation and palliative care? How do we promote and support individuals in understanding their responsibility for 'prudent care' of their own lives and health? How vigilant are we in assessing the justice implications of health system changes? What lessons are there in this story for our cooperation with the broader health system? What are the limits of cooperation if we are to be truly good Samaritans?

Finally, the story tells us, the Samaritan commits to follow-up of the injured man. He has made a commitment to care and recognizes the importance of seeing that commitment through to the restoration of function.

How do we balance response to the needs of individuals with responsible stewardship of shared resources and promotion of the common good? How do we organize the systems that must respond to health needs today?

*How attentive are we to the burdens of long-term care
on families and communities?*

Promoting and restoring wholeness of life means not only treating
symptoms but being attentive to the causes of suffering and injustice
and the long-term needs of the community. The tradition sees the
quality of relationships and the protection of human rights within
community as basic to a healthy, just society. It emphasizes the
link between promoting health and working to overcome injustice.

- Respect for the rights of persons and communities is
  basic to any sense of justice. Such rights are an
  expression of respect for human dignity.

- The needs of the vulnerable and abandoned are to be
  given preferential attention. Their well-being measures
  the moral quality of any community or organization.
  This specific love of the poor is at the heart of the
  Gospel message and the building of God's kingdom.

- Health includes physiological, psychological, spiritual,
  social, economic and ecological considerations. The
  promotion of justice includes attending to all these
  dimensions of health.

- We are called to foster the common good, which is
  understood to be the sum total of social conditions that
  promote the human flourishing of all.

RESPONDING TO THE GOSPEL CALL FOR COMPASSION AND HEALING SERVICE

As Jesus points out in the story of the Good Samaritan, we are called to be "neighbours" to one another and to offer compassionate care and healing. Thus, the Gospel call to charity and love is expressed in compassion and solidarity with those in need. Through the centuries, Christians, and indeed people of all faith traditions, have generously responded to persons who suffer in any way. Motivated by their faith, Christians have specifically brought to the fields of education, social services and health care a long tradition of dedicated service, loving care and a high degree of excellence. Charity, compassion, caring, trust and justice are all foundational values in any authentic Christian approach to health care and the healing of human suffering.

Catholic health and social service organizations are a visible expression of the compassion and healing ministry of Christ and so bear witness to the Good News of the Gospel as expressed in the Catholic faith tradition. These organizations have a distinct spiritual vision and culture that directs them to attend with compassion and dignity to the needs of poor and vulnerable individuals. They fulfill this important role by being present to people at critical points where their lives can be fostered, namely, where they are born and die, where they are cured and healed, and where they are assisted when in trouble. The Catholic tradition sees this concrete involvement as a sacramental presence, an encounter with Christ. It is that vision which defines the quality of their relationship with those in need of care.

Our distinctive vocation in Christian health care is not so much to heal better or more efficiently than anyone else; it is to bring comfort to people by giving them

*an experience that will strengthen their confidence in
life. The ultimate goal of our care is to give those who
are ill, through our care, a reason to hope.*[4]

This hope involves healing for human persons in all their dimensions
and includes attention to the meaning of human life, its joys and
sorrows, its suffering and death, and its spiritual value in the eyes
of God. A Catholic perspective respects both body and spirit, the
individual good and the common good, the person and the
community, personal faith and belonging to an organized Church
that can speak with authority and encouragement.

In society at large, Catholic health and social service organizations
are a voice expressing a vision of life based on the moral and
religious values of the Catholic tradition. The care provided by
these organizations is one expression within the local Church of
the healing ministry of Jesus Christ.

THE CALL TO COMPASSION AND ETHICAL REFLECTION

The Catholic moral tradition seeks to understand how charity and
compassion can be lived most authentically in response to the
concrete realities of daily life. The tradition recognizes that "without
truth, charity degenerates into sentimentality."[5] Charity and truth
are linked, and thus charity "needs to be understood, confirmed
and practiced in the light of truth."[6] One of the objectives of this

---

4.   Joseph Cardinal Bernardin,, Pastoral Letter, "A Sign of Hope" (1995);
     quoted in his article "What Makes a Hospital Catholic – A Response,"
     America, Vol. 174, no. 15 (May 4, 1996), 9.

5.   Pope Benedict XVI, Encyclical Letter *Caritas in Veritate* (*Charity in
     Truth*), Vatican, 2009, no. 3. *Note*: All Vatican documents may be accessed
     through the Vatican publishing house website at: http://www.vatican.va.

Health Ethics Guide is to seek out and express how best the call to compassion and healing can respond to truth as found in the Catholic faith tradition.

This tradition includes a number of theological foundations that guide ethical reflection. These include the conviction that all of creation is a gift of God's love, something we do not own but care for; an acceptance of the Catholic Church's authority to teach definitively on moral issues; a belief in the presence of God in human experience; an awareness that we have a responsibility to work to eliminate sickness and suffering using both science and technology as well as other long-standing or innovative means of healing and care; an acknowledgement that suffering can have meaning and value for human growth; and the recognition that the moral dimension of human existence requires that we act with a fully informed conscience.

The local bishop has the responsibility to provide leadership in fostering the mission of Catholic organizations. In this regard, he exercises responsibilities that are rooted in his office as teacher, priest and pastor, and coordinates the ministries in the local church.[7] In fulfilling his role as the primary teacher of the local faith community, he has the task of ensuring that the teaching of the Catholic Church is reflected faithfully in the context of rapidly developing medical advances and of the increasing complexity of the human sciences. In this task, he may consult with specialists in different disciplines. Nevertheless, in areas where the Church has not taken a position on an ethical issue, the faithful should "not

---

6. Ibid., no. 2.

7. United States Conference of Catholic Bishops (USCCB), *Ethical and Religious Directives for Catholic Health Care Services*, Washington, D.C., 2009, General Introduction.

imagine that their pastors are always such experts, that to every problem which arises, however complicated, they can readily give a concrete solution, or even that such is their mission. Rather, enlightened by Christian wisdom and giving close attention to the teaching authority of the Church, let them take on their own distinctive role."[8]

As priest, the diocesan bishop has responsibility for and oversees the sacramental ministry to those being cared for. As pastor, the local bishop encourages the faithful in the healing ministry of the Church and witnesses, along with the faithful, to the values of respecting dignity, fostering trust and promoting justice. These responsibilities will require that Catholic health care providers and the diocesan bishop engage in ongoing communication on ethical and pastoral matters that require his attention.

The quality of ethical decisions depends not merely on abstract reasoning, but on the lived faith, experience, prudence and virtue of everyone involved in each issue being discussed. They "should also know that it is generally the function of their well-formed Christian conscience to see that the divine law is inscribed in the life of the earthly city ..."[9] The Catholic moral tradition is the fruit of an ongoing dialogue between our understanding of human nature and creation and our experience of God as revealed in Jesus Christ. This dialogue develops through prayer, study, reflection, and recognition of the working of the Spirit in the experience of health and Christian communities as they grapple with difficult issues. The dialogue is aided by others, such as moral theologians, ethicists and pastoral care workers. The results of this dialogue are

---

8. Second Vatican Council, *Gaudium et Spes* (*Pastoral Constitution on the Church in the Modern World*), no. 43.

9. Ibid, no.43.

enlightened and informed by reflection on Sacred Scripture and especially by the long tradition of Church teaching, with the diocesan bishop as the primary interpreter of that teaching to the local faith community. The goal of this striving for truth is to find the course of action that best shows compassion and best serves the total well-being of the individual person in need of healing or care.

Catholic moral tradition is a living tradition. Its formulations are necessarily the product of a grasp of reality that is constantly being refined due to historically conditioned attitudes, insights and an ever-developing scientific and philosophical understanding of health care concerns. Although key ethical imperatives (such as respect for human life) remain constant, the concrete application of these imperatives always has to be worked out in the concrete, here and now.

The Catholic tradition is not always clear or unanimous concerning all moral issues. Uncertainty about the morally correct course of action in a particular case may arise from several sources. The facts as ascertained from clinical experience and other scientific means may remain in doubt. The way in which moral rules apply to a particular case where one rule seems to conflict with another may also not be clear. Furthermore, in some cases responsible experts may continue to differ on certain general rules of thumb, and the Church Magisterium may choose not to speak authoritatively on the point. In such situations of uncertain obligations, one should follow one's duly informed conscience. (See *Appendix I.*)

FUNDAMENTAL MORAL VALUES

In the Judeo-Christian tradition, and many other traditions also, the core moral duty persons owe each other is to "love one another" to be "neighbour" to the other as set out in the parable of the Good Samaritan. That core Gospel value gives rise to the call to respect dignity, the call to foster trust and the call to promote justice. These aspects of charity or compassion can be expanded to highlight other more specific values that help direct ethical discernment and decision making. These values are not, for the most part, unique to Catholic health care, but they are essential for faithfulness to the Catholic tradition.

The Call to Respect Dignity

1. **Respect for the dignity of every human person** – The lives of all persons possess an inherent dignity and worth that is independent of that which any other person or the State may bestow upon them.[10] The basis for this dignity, in the Judeo-Christian tradition, is the belief that every human being is made in the image of God (see *Genesis* 1:27). In the provision of health and social services this value becomes the basis for the requirements around informed consent, privacy and confidentiality.

2. **Respect for all human life** – All human life is a gift of God's love and the prerequisite for all other human goods. It is to be respected from conception until natural death. Nevertheless, the preservation of human life is not an absolute good, and may be forgone, for example, in defense of others or in allowing death to come by not using means to preserve life that are overly burdensome or ineffective.

10. Ibid., nos. 27-29.

The Call to Foster Trust

3. The interconnectedness of every human being – Trust both requires and establishes relationship. Human persons are social beings and normally cannot live or develop their potential outside of human relationships and community.[11] This fundamental value affirms that every person is interconnected with every human being, with all of creation and with God.

4. Stewardship and creativity – Human persons are in relationship not only with each other but with all of creation. The Scriptures present a view of creation as both gift and responsibility. All of creation is God's gift to us. Consequently, as stewards of creation, we share a responsibility to respect, protect and care for all of the environment and for ourselves. We are to use our own free and intelligent creativity to discover the benefits of nature both around us and in our own persons, while humbly respecting any limitations inherent in it.[12]

The Call to Promote Justice

5. Justice – Justice is to give to the other what is that person's due. It is recognition and respect for the legitimate rights of others. "Not only is justice not extraneous to charity, ... justice is inseparable from charity and intrinsic to it."[13]

6. The common good – This fundamental value is central to the Catholic tradition and has recently been re-emphasized. "Besides the good of the individual, there is a good that is

---

11. Ibid., nos. 12, 25.

12. See Pope Benedict XVI, Encyclical Letter *Caritas in Veritate (Charity in Truth)*, Vatican, 2009, nos. 48-51.

linked to living in society .... It is the good of 'all of us', made up of individuals, families and intermediate groups who together constitute society. It is the good that is sought not for its own sake, but for the people who belong to the social community and who can only really and effectively pursue their good within it. To desire the common good and strive towards it is a requirement of justice and charity."[14] It is the building of a just and compassionate social order in which true human development is encouraged. By extension, the common good includes respect for the environment as well.

7. Solidarity – Solidarity is "first and foremost a sense of responsibility on the part of everyone with regard to everyone, and it cannot be merely relegated to the state."[15] It is more than the political overtones it has had in some countries, but carries vast socio-economic implications for our world and health care today. It is directly related to charity. For example, papal teaching[16] has used it as another way to speak of charity in regard to the justification for certain kinds of organ transplants.

THE HEALTH ETHICS GUIDE

This Introduction provides the context in which the rest of the *Health Ethics Guide* is to be understood. The goal of the *Health Ethics Guide* is threefold:

    1. to remind readers of the fundamental commitment within

---

13. Ibid., no. 6.

14. Ibid., no. 7.

15. Ibid., no. 38.

16. See Pope John Paul II, "Address to Participants of the First International Congress of the Society for Organ Sharing," 20 June 1991.

the Catholic tradition to the ministry of caring for those who are sick and suffering;

2. to articulate the values and principles found within that tradition by providing guidelines for ethical decision making; and

3. to promote a pastoral understanding of how these principles and values can guide decision making in health and social services.

This *Health Ethics Guide* proceeds with a description of the social nature of care in Chapter One. Chapter Two explores the foundational notion of the dignity of the human person and its implications for health and social services.

The next three chapters address specific moral and ethical issues at the beginning of life (Chapter Three), end-of-life care (Chapter Four), and organ donation (Chapter Five). Chapter Six outlines Catholic considerations related to research with human subjects, while Chapter Seven discusses governance and administration issues encountered in operating Catholic health and social service organizations.

In order to assist the lived application of this guide, an appendix is provided to explore the notion of conscience as well as some of the key principles developed within the Catholic tradition for making ethical decisions when values appear to be in conflict. A second appendix provides a glossary of terms used in the *Health Ethics Guide*.

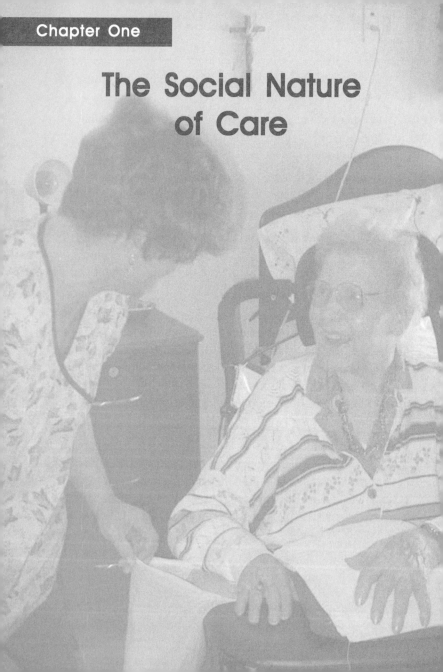

Chapter One

The Social Nature of Care

Introductory Comments

The parable of the Good Samaritan demonstrates dramatically that the provision of health care requires responses from individuals, organizations and society as a whole. The Samaritan gave a courageous personal response, but he needed others to assist in the provision of all the care that the injured man needed.This is a challenging reminder that health care has intrinsically social and relational dimensions.

Not surprisingly, then, health care and other service organizations operate in societies that are organized into complex networks of social groups, from the smallest family to local, national, international and global systems. These different social structures are contemporary expressions of the basic and diverse social needs of all persons. The social interdependence of all human beings, and the interconnectedness of all of creation, is a fundamental truth and central tenet of Catholic social justice teaching.

Christian tradition uses the images of the human body and of the family to emphasize this social interdependence. Every person shares responsibility for our society and society has a responsibility for each of its members. As Christians, we also live in society as members of a community of faith. The faith life of the Christian community is shaped by our baptismal call to share God's life and to work for the common good of all peoples. The fundamental law of this community is such that love of God, love of neighbour and love of self should not be separated.

The individual and social needs of people always must be kept in balance within a social order "founded on truth, built on justice, and animated by love .... Every social group must take account of the needs and legitimate aspirations of other groups, and even of the general welfare of the entire human family."[1] Catholic social teaching expresses this concern for the welfare of all in terms of a global solidarity. "There is no progress toward the complete development of men and women without the simultaneous development of all humanity in the spirit of solidarity."[2]

HEALTH CARE

Illness and disease are human conditions that require a particular manifestation of solidarity and collective response. As Pope John XXIII reminded all: " …a human being has the right to security in sickness."[3] While there are many different approaches to the organization of health and social services, some basic principles are clear.

Specifically, health-care justice obliges a society to provide all its citizens with an appropriate level of health care. Maintaining both universality and the accessibility of comprehensive health care remains a prime objective of health-care justice. The grounds for deciding who gets health care cannot be based on merit, social worth, or the ability to pay. Everyone has the right to health care.[4]

---

1. Second Vatican Council, *Gaudium et Spes* (*Pastoral Constitution on the Church in the Modern World*), Vatican, 1965, no. 25.

2. Pope Paul VI, Encyclical Letter *Populorum Progressio (On the Development of Peoples)*, Vatican, 1967, no. 43.

3. Pope John XXIII, Encyclical Letter *Pacem in Terris* (*Peace on Earth*), Vatican, 1963, no. 11.

4. Canadian Conference of Catholic Bishops, *Catholic Health Care Ministry in Canada,* 2005 Pastoral Letter by the Permanent Council of the CCCB, no. 10.

For this reason, the Catholic tradition views health care as an essential social good, a service to persons in need and a component of the common good. Health care is not, and should not be treated as, a mere commodity exchanged for profit, to which access depends on an ability to pay.

Pope Benedict XVI, in his encyclical *Caritas in Veritate*, indicates clearly that life ethics must be linked explicitly to social ethics.[5] Health concerns are not limited to the needs of individuals. The determinants of health include biological and psychological (mental and emotional) factors, the physical environment, lifestyle, spirituality and religious belief, social interactions and support, economic status, and working conditions. Together, these factors influence the health of individuals and communities.

> *It is therefore necessary that [governments] give wholehearted and careful attention to the social as well as to the economic progress of the citizens, and to the development ...of such essential services as ...housing, public health, education ...*[6]

THE CATHOLIC VISION OF HEALTH AND SOCIAL SERVICE

The Catholic tradition recognizes that as social creatures of body and spirit, people need not only individual activity, but also outward, tangible human institutions to help them live as a believing community, bearing witness to the Good News of the Gospel as

---

5. Pope Benedict XVI, Encyclical Letter *Caritas in Veritate (Charity in Truth)*, Vatican, 2009, nos. 34-42.

6. Pope John XXIII, Encyclical Letter *Pacem in Terris* (*Peace on Earth*), Vatican, 1963, no. 64.

expressed in the Catholic faith tradition. Catholic organizations fulfill this important role by being present to people at critical points in their lives.

Catholic health and social service organizations are among the apostolic activities for which the diocesan bishop bears pastoral responsibility and authority. Among the tangible signs that should characterize Catholic organizations are: Catholic sponsorship and management; recognition by the local bishop of such organizations as an integral part of the apostolate of the Church; quality care; careful stewardship of resources; a culture that supports Catholic ethical values and spiritual beliefs; promotion of spiritual/religious care; mission and values integration; just working conditions; and the availability of the sacraments and the prominence of Christian art, signs and symbols. As a core expression of their identity, Catholic organizations privilege the spiritual for all those they serve and, for Catholics in particular, they cooperate as fully as possible with the local bishop in fulfilling his responsibility to provide sacramental care.

Catholic health care facilities in Canada form an integral part of Canada's health care system. In fact, they have played an important role of leadership and pioneering service in the health care field since the beginning of our country's history. They are a strong testimony to the profound faith, charity and generosity of the religious women and men who founded them, and they continue to be a witness to the healing compassion of Christ.

Catholic health and social services should therefore be distinguished by their commitment to work for justice in health and social service. They seek to serve and to advocate for those who are marginalized in society, witnessing to a special obligation to the poor and vulnerable. All those who are engaged in this ministry seek to create a community of compassion.

Catholic health and social service organizations function in civil society with a particular identity and mission. The specific way in which this mission is carried out distinguishes the service of Catholic care providers. This service is designated as "ministry" because it is motivated by the Gospel and is part of an enduring faith tradition. This understanding of ministry challenges any system that might treat a person merely as a case, number or statistic. The care provided by these organizations is understood as a continuation in the healing ministry of Jesus, motivated by a particular vision based on the moral and religious values of the Catholic tradition.

> Catholic health and social service providers belong to communities of service dedicated to the promotion of a healthy society. As members of these communities, they contribute a perspective inspired by the example of Jesus and guided by the Roman Catholic tradition. Those who exercise this ministry serve others, and themselves require a community of support.

HEALTH AND HEALING

1. Since life and health are gifts of God, "we must take reasonable care of them, taking into account the needs of others and the common good."[7] (Refer to articles 16, 39, 51, 76, 77, 89.)

2. Health arises from the dynamic balance and harmony of a person's biological, psychological and spiritual energies

---

7. *Catechism of the Catholic Church,* English Translation, Libreria Editrice Vaticana, Concacan Inc., Ottawa, 1997; no. 2288.

within a physical, social, cultural and economic environment. Health is not merely the absence of illness, but the full functioning of the person as an integrated whole. (Refer to articles 4, 16.)

3. All persons have a responsibility to make personal lifestyle choices that will have a positive effect on their health and well-being, and to participate in the promotion of the health of the local and global community. (Refer to article 1.)

4. We share a responsibility to ensure that the primary purpose of our socioeconomic order should be to develop our resources to serve the basic needs of all people for a fully human life. (Refer to article 11.)

    "Concern for the health of its citizens requires that society help in the attainment of living conditions that allow them to grow and reach maturity: food and clothing, housing, health care, basic education, employment and social assistance."[8]

5. Commitment to global solidarity ought to move us to be sensitive to environmental issues and their effects on health and well-being. (Refer to article 13.)

CHRISTIAN HEALING MINISTRY

6. Healing is more than simply curing a disease. Healing takes into account the wholeness of the person, recognizing the interrelationship of body, mind and spirit. Healing involves the restoration of balance and acknowledges the role that spirituality and/or religious belief can play in the healing process.

---

8. Ibid., no.2288.

7.   For Christians, health care is a supremely human enterprise. But it is also regarded as an effort to cooperate with God's healing power, which is at work reaching out to make persons whole. Healing is seen as a ministry in which all are called to participate as part of their baptismal commitment. Some people have dedicated themselves to particular expressions of the healing ministry by assuming responsibilities as professionals, support workers and volunteers. These people are a visible sign and reminder to the broader community of this ministry. (Refer to articles 141, 142.)

MISSION OF CATHOLIC HEALTH AND SOCIAL SERVICE ORGANIZATIONS

8.   The mission and religious identity of every Catholic organization is rooted in the moral values, principles and teachings of the Catholic tradition. The organization's mission should be articulated clearly in a mission statement. Such statements should be reviewed regularly, with opportunities for input from all members of the organization, in order to ensure fidelity to the mission. (Refer to articles 144-150.)

9.   Whatever its particular objectives, every Catholic health and social service organization aims primarily at the relief of suffering and the promotion of health in all its dimensions – physical, emotional and spiritual. The breadth of this mission is demonstrated through the integration of policies and programs that emphasize well-being, spiritual care, the promotion of the health of individuals and communities, the prevention of disease, rehabilitation, and the care of people with acute, chronic or terminal illnesses. This model necessitates collaboration among a variety of agencies, and interactions between the health care and social service

systems and other sectors in society, such as education, housing, religious groups, unions and professional organizations. (Refer to articles 146, 150-152, 184.)

10. Catholic health and social service organizations should be characterized by an atmosphere that promotes healing and by a spirit of compassion that is rooted in human solidarity and in fidelity to the healing mission of Christ. All care providers are to foster an environment that is marked by the promotion of human dignity, trust and justice in their provision of care. (Refer to articles 167-170.)

SOCIAL RESPONSIBILITY

11. Health care is a fundamental human good that is necessary for human flourishing. Accordingly, there is a fundamental difference between the provision of health care and the production and distribution of commodities. The not-for-profit structure is the preferred model for delivering health care services because it is uniquely designed to provide equitable access to essential human services and to promote the common good. (Refer to articles 4, 151, 180.)

12. In accord with social justice teaching, Catholic health and social service should distinguish itself by service to and advocacy for those people whose social condition puts them at the margins of our society and makes them particularly vulnerable to discrimination. (Refer to articles 66, 115, 147, 151.)

13. The "environment is God's gift to everyone, and in our use of it we have a responsibility towards the poor, towards future generations, and towards humanity as a whole."[9] Because we

"cannot interfere in one area of the ecosystem without paying due attention both to the consequences of such interference in other areas and to the well-being of future generations,"[10] all have a special obligation to be aware of the larger environmental implications of health care delivery and especially of certain drugs and their potential harms, and to be committed to reducing the burden on the environment that comes from delivery of this health care. (Refer to article 5.)

COMMITMENT TO EDUCATION AND RESEARCH

14. Catholic health and social service organizations recognize the importance of education as part of their mandate, especially in the following areas: care and responsibility for one's health and well-being; staff development; the education of students in the caring professions; and public education in health promotion and disease prevention. This education is marked by ongoing reflection on the Christian meaning of suffering, illness, health, morality, life and death. (Refer to articles 37, 42, 142, 145.)

15. Catholic health and social service organizations are part of a tradition that encourages the use of wisdom and compassion in the pursuit of research into new methods and treatments for bringing healing to those in need. In keeping with their mission and purpose, these organizations also recognize the importance of research for improving the quality of care.

---

9. Pope Benedict XVI, Encyclical Letter *Caritas in Veritate* (*Charity in Truth*), Vatican, 2009, no. 48.

10. Pope John Paul II, "The Ecological Crisis: A Common Responsibility," in *Peace with God the Creator, Peace with All of Creation*: Message for the Celebration of the World Day of Peace, Vatican, 1990, no. 6.

While research can result in great advances in care, it often brings complex ethical concerns regarding its aims and use. Research activities must be guided by approved ethical standards, and cannot be pursued at the expense of such values as respect for human life and dignity, fostering trust in care, and justice. (Refer to Chapter 6.)

Chapter Two

Dignity of the Human Person

Introductory Comments

Rooted in charity, Catholic health and social services are called to respect the dignity of persons, to foster trust and to promote justice. This chapter focuses on specific aspects of the call to respect the dignity of persons. The dignity of human persons is rooted in their relationship with God, and in their being created in God's image and likeness.[1] They are called to seek the good through love of God and love of neighbour.[2] Human persons are created with a radical capacity for intelligence and free will, along with moral consciousness and a potential for self-fulfillment. They possess a fundamental capacity to know, to love, to choose freely, to determine the direction of their lives and to seek the good. Each person is irreplaceable, with an inherent value and purpose in life. This respect for the dignity of each human person has been acknowledged and enshrined in the United Nations' *Universal Declaration of Human Rights*.[3] In light of Gospel values, differences of age, sex, race, religion, social and cultural background, health status, sexual orientation, intelligence, economic status, employment, mental capacity or other distinctions do not take away from the inherent dignity shared by all persons. Persons who are marginalized in society because of a physical or mental condition, or because of social, cultural or economic factors, are frequently stigmatized. The Catholic tradition maintains that

---

1. *Catechism of the Catholic Church*, English Translation, Libreria Editrice Vaticana, Concacan Inc., Ottawa, 1997, nos. 357, 1700.

2. Second Vatican Council, *Gaudium et Spes* (*Pastoral Constitution on the Church in the Modern World*), Vatican, 1965, nos. 12-19.

3. General Assembly of the United Nations, *The Universal Declaration of Human Rights* (December 10, 1948).

they are to be treated with equal respect and compassion. (Refer to articles 16, 27, 28, 83, 84.)

> The inherent dignity of each person is to be upheld by treating all persons with equal respect.

RESPECT FOR EVERY PERSON

16. All persons have equal dignity and are to be treated with equal respect, especially when they are weak, vulnerable or sick. The Church's social teaching recognizes that this respect for persons requires that they be provided with the health care they need " …for the proper development of life."[4] This duty is, nevertheless, limited by what can fairly be provided given the mission of the health care organization and the overall common good. (Refer to articles 8, 10, 25, 66, 92, 151-153, 169, 171.)

THE PRIMARY ROLE OF THE PERSON RECEIVING CARE

17. Persons who are receiving care and who have the capacity to make their own decisions are the primary decision makers with respect to proposed treatment and care options. They have a right to know the state of their own health. They should also be able to expect relationships with health care professionals that are marked by mutual respect, trust, honesty

---

4. Pope John XXIII, Encyclical Letter *Pacem in Terris* (*Peace on Earth*), Vatican, 1963, no. 11.

and confidentiality. Health and social service organizations have a responsibility to provide persons receiving care and health care professionals with the necessary information, counselling and spiritual support required to make decisions according to a well-formed conscience. When making decisions, persons receiving care should be helped to consider how the proposed treatment may affect their personal vocation or overall responsibilities in life. (Refer to articles 18-20, 70-72, 92, 114.)

INFORMED DECISION MAKING

18. The informed consent of a person receiving care is necessary for any health care procedure. Informed decision making requires that the person be provided with all the information necessary for making a sound decision. This includes information about the benefits, risks and any potential harm of a proposed treatment, possible alternatives and the option of no treatment at all. A health professional skilled in communication, who can respond to questions from the person receiving care and, when appropriate, their family, should give this information in an atmosphere of honesty and concern. Such information should be given face to face and in a suitable environment. Health care professionals should confirm that the person receiving care understands and appreciates the information being conveyed and is thus capable of making a decision, and that the decision is being made voluntarily. (Refer to articles 55, 58, 65, 70, 71, 92-94, 96, 114, 123.)

19. For those persons receiving care who do not have the capacity to make their own decisions, an informed decision is to be obtained from an authorized surrogate who is able to speak to the wishes, values and beliefs of the person receiving

care. Wishes, values and beliefs of the person receiving care expressed previously, either orally or through advance care planning documents, should normally be followed in making surrogate decisions.[5] In emergency situations, if the patient or surrogate is unable to provide an informed decision, treatment decisions made by health professionals should keep in mind the wishes, values and beliefs that the patient expressed previously when capable or, if these are not known, the patient's overall best interests. (Refer to articles 72-74, 91, 93, 125.)

20.   While persons who are capable of making their own decisions have a legal right to refuse or withdraw consent to any care or treatment including life-saving or life-sustaining treatment, they do have a moral obligation to seek those measures for preserving life that offer a reasonable hope of benefit and are not unduly burdensome as determined by the person receiving care. (Refer to articles 1, 26, 76-79, 84, 89.)

PRIVACY AND CONFIDENTIALITY OF INFORMATION

21.   Every person has a right to privacy and confidentiality concerning all personal health information. Care must be taken to restrict the availability of such records to authorized persons only. Personal health information should only be shared or disclosed when authorized to do so by the person receiving care or by an authorized surrogate or when authorized by law. In particular, special precautions are to be taken to protect the confidentiality of records, files, computer data and other information that could pose a serious

---

5.   See article 73 for specific issues regarding decision making in the care of children.

threat of discrimination or other adverse social consequences. However, privacy and confidentiality are limited when they endanger the health and well-being of others or when the law requires disclosure (e.g., mandatory reporting of gunshot wounds, or reporting of suspected child or elder abuse). (Refer to articles 58, 121, 127, 136.)

EMOTIONAL AND FAMILY BONDS

22. Family and close friends are intended to be the privileged bearers of intimacy, loving support, courage and compassion in the face of illness and suffering. This support is an expression of the community's healing presence. For Christians, it is a tangible manifestation of the healing presence of God. Efforts are to be taken to strengthen and support such relationships in their healing and wellness roles. (Refer to articles 65, 67.)

23. Each person's emotional, familial, cultural and spiritual relationships are to be respected and fostered. These relationships create rights and duties both for the person receiving services and for those providing care. (Refer to article 65.)

SPIRITUAL AND RELIGIOUS CARE

24. Spiritual and religious care, often referred to as pastoral care, is integral to the healing process. Catholic health and social service organizations should ensure that such services are provided. Good spiritual and religious care is characterized by sensitivity and respect for the varying spiritual and religious needs of the recipients and for the spiritual suffering that often accompanies sickness. It also provides opportunities to participate in the life of a faith community. Family and informal

caregivers require a similar kind of support. (Refer to articles 154, 155.)

RESPECT FOR VARYING CULTURES AND TRADITIONS

25. Catholic health and social service organizations will care for all, regardless of religion, socioeconomic status or culture. They will respect the variety of cultures and religious traditions of those they serve and those who work within their organizations, given that they will not be compelled to provide any service that is inconsistent with their Catholic identity and mission statement or that fails to meet standards for quality care. They must also be committed to developing cultural competence within the organization, i.e., knowing about the cultural customs and traditions of the populations being served and being sensitive to these while caring for the individual. (Refer to articles 16, 23, 71, 74, 107.)

CONSCIENTIOUS OBJECTION

26. Health care and other professionals should not be expected to participate in procedures that are contrary to their professional judgement or to their conscience or that are contrary to the values or mission of their organization. However, they must not abandon those to whom they provide care. (Refer to articles 80-82, 91, 163, 165.)

INADEQUATE OR INAPPROPRIATE DISCHARGE

27. Persons receiving care should not be transferred or discharged by the care provider until there is assurance that the person is safe in leaving the service, either because they are able to care for themselves or because adequate supports have been put in place. Similarly, those who no longer require

the level of care provided by a given organization should be transferred to a more appropriate place of care when it is available. There are sometimes circumstances around discharge that may challenge a person's dignity, such as the discharge of a homeless person. Such situations are a call to the community to seek solutions. (Refer to articles 10, 12.)

MENTAL HEALTH

28. Mental health is fundamental to a person's well-being. There are intimate connections among mental health, one's general attitude to life, and the healing process. Care providers must attend to the mental health needs of the person receiving care. Furthermore, a person's mental state should never be the cause of their not receiving necessary, compassionate care. (Refer to articles 12, 16.)

29. Any form of treatment that restricts personal freedom or hinders a person's mental capacity, such as commitment to a mental institution or the administration of drugs that affect the person's mental functions, are only to be implemented for the good of the person receiving care and/or when the safety of others is in danger. Such treatments should always seek the person's greater freedom and functioning and be done with scrupulous observance of due legal process. (Refer to article 30.)

RESTRAINTS

30. Since the use of restraints can be an infringement of a person's dignity, a policy of least restraint should be adopted. Restraints may be necessary when behaviour presents an unacceptable potential for injury to the person receiving care or to others. Such measures should only be undertaken if all

other alternative safety measures have proven ineffective, the right of freedom of movement of the individual has been taken into consideration, and the safety needs of the person receiving care or of others outweigh the potential negative effects of restraint use. (Refer to articles 16, 29.)

ABUSE OF PERSONS RECEIVING CARE

31. Care providers are to be trained to recognize the symptoms of violence and abuse and to respond with compassion and sensitivity. A protocol is to be established in conformity with legal requirements to deal with all forms of abuse. Special attention is to be given to groups more vulnerable to abuse. It is recommended that such a protocol also address situations of abuse among care providers and between care providers and those receiving care. (Refer to article 12.)

CARE OF THOSE ASSAULTED

32. A protocol to assist those who have been subjected to sexual assault is to be established. Health care providers should cooperate with law enforcement officials when appropriate or required by law and offer the person psychological and spiritual support as well as accurate medical information. A female who has been raped should be able to defend herself against the possibility of conception from the sexual assault.[6] If, after appropriate testing, there is no evidence that conception has occurred already, those treatments that would

---

6. United States Conference of Catholic Bishops (USCCB), *Ethical and Religious Directives for Catholic Health Care Services*, Washington, D.C., 2009, Directive 36: Also, a note to this directive suggests that women be advised of ethical restrictions that prevent Catholic hospitals from using abortifacient procedures.

prevent ovulation, sperm capacitation or fertilization are permitted. Those treatments that cause the removal of, destruction of or interference with the implantation of a fertilized ovum are not permitted. Where the state of scientific knowledge is inconclusive as to possible abortifacient effects of a treatment, it should not be used. In all cases, health care providers should always show compassion and sensitivity to the person assaulted.[7]

PROMOTION OF DIGNITY REGARDING SEXUALITY AND PERSONS RECEIVING CARE

33. Sexuality is an integral part of being human. Human sexuality is expressed through personal grooming habits, dress, touch, companionship, the personalization of one's environment, and intimate physical affection. This irreducible dimension of the person is to be treated with respect and sensitivity. (Refer to articles 16, 21.)

34. In institutional settings, it is crucial to respect the deeply personal nature of sexuality, to balance the needs of the individual with the needs of other members of the institutional community, and to respect the values of the Catholic organization. (Refer to article 21.)

35. Guidelines are important for responding to situations when it is determined that an individual who lacks decision-making capacity has entered a sexual relationship with another, or whose sexual activity is causing concern or distress among care providers, family members or other persons receiving

---

7. Regarding applications of this guideline and the approval of the diocesan Bishop, see page xi in the Preamble.

care. Such guidelines should seek creative, respectful and ethical resolutions for all concerned, in keeping with the institution's Catholic identity. (Refer to articles 21, 33.)

GENDER REASSIGNMENT

36. All individuals suffering from any form of gender identification difficulties, especially gender dysphoria, are to be seen as children of God and treated with compassionate pastoral care. They are to receive objective counselling respecting the totality and integrity of their personhood in the complexity of their condition and of how they see themselves. Such counselling respects the value of the psychological and spiritual support needed to try to achieve integration in their being. Surgical interventions, hormonal therapy and referrals for sexual reassignment are inconsistent with Catholic teaching regarding the principles of totality and integrity and thus should not be performed in Catholic facilities. (Refer to article 16.)

SEXUALITY AND PUBLIC HEALTH

37. Health care organizations, parishes and schools should assist families in providing education that respects Catholic teaching concerning sexuality and public health, including comprehensive and accurate information about sexually transmitted diseases. They should also provide compassionate care for those who suffer from these diseases. (Refer to articles 33, 34.)

Chapter Three

Care at the Beginning of Life

Introductory Comments

Rooted in charity, Catholic health and social services are called to respect the dignity of persons, to foster trust and to promote justice. This chapter focuses on these three calls as they affect issues of care at the beginning of life. From conception to natural death, every human being deserves respect and the societal safeguards that allow life to flourish. Men and women image the Trinitarian relationships of Father, Son and Holy Spirit, implying generativity, communication and self-giving love. Such loving relationships lead to a personalist norm, namely, that all persons are to be loved for their own sake and never to be simply used as a means to some other end.

The primary and most intimate human relationship instituted by the Creator is that embodied in the marriage of man and woman. This relationship unfolds as a faithful bond or covenant, a communion of persons in which a man and a woman become "one flesh." God created this human sexuality as good. Through it, we enjoy the personal aspect of our identity that gives beauty, pleasure and mystery to our lives. Embedded in human sexual activity are certain fundamental "givens." Human sexual intercourse has an inherent two-fold meaning: it is a union of love between a husband and wife (the unitive meaning), and it expresses an overflowing love open to accepting new life (the procreative meaning). Thus, the self-giving love for each other is often completed and enhanced by the gift of children, entrusted by God to parents for care, nurture and formation. Every child, therefore, deserves to enter life within the context of marriage.

This personal and relational nature of marriage and family underlies the Catholic evaluation of all biomedical methods and technologies used to protect and assist human life. Nonetheless, Catholic health care seeks to demonstrate loving compassion, tolerance and sensitivity to those who disagree with or are unable to live up to these challenging teachings as seen within the Catholic tradition and understood by human reason.

Catholic teaching recognizes that different philosophical approaches and science do not agree exactly when, in the process of conception and development, a human embryo becomes a person.[1] Nevertheless, Catholic teaching emphasizes that a human embryo enjoys inherent dignity from God and is to be treated as a person from conception.

Parents are called to practise responsible parenthood, by prayerfully considering the number of children they can lovingly and prudently support in their own unique circumstances, and by planning their family with the use of morally acceptable means that respect their own dignity and the dignity of every human being, right from conception.

New biomedical technologies possess not only unprecedented hopes for therapeutic interventions in health care but also enormous dangers. Some people may see Church teachings in these areas as containing too many prohibitions. Yet, "Behind every 'no' in the difficult task of discerning between good and evil, there shines a great 'Yes' to the recognition of the dignity and inalienable value of every single and unique human being called into

---

1. See Congregation for the Doctrine of the Faith, *Donum Vitae (Gift of Life) – Instruction on Respect for Human Life in its Origin and on the Dignity of Procreation – Replies to Certain Questions of the Day,* Vatican, 1987, I.1.

existence."[2] This human dignity is often sacrificed in our utilitarian culture. Respecting "the wonder of ourselves" (Psalm 139:14) in the eyes of God can inspire and guide us all in these teachings associated with the beginning of life.

> Human personhood, including our sexuality, has a special significance and sacredness given by the Creator. This sacred dimension of the person calls us to treat every human being, from conception to natural death, with honour, respect and justice.

HEALTH ISSUES UNIQUE TO WOMEN

38. Special concern will be shown for health issues unique to women and the complete integrity of their bodies. Moral issues around sexuality and technology arise, in particular, with regard to the conception, gestation and birth of children. Being pregnant is not a disease. When pregnant women present themselves for health care services, health care practitioners must be concerned for the life and integrity both of these women and of their children.

RESPONSIBLE PARENTHOOD TO BE FOSTERED

39. The dignity of human sexuality is rooted in the two-fold desire for both unity with another in a deeply intimate and exclusive

---

2. Congregation for the Doctrine of the Faith, Instruction *Dignitas Personae* (*Dignity of the Person*) on Certain Bioethical Questions, Vatican, 2008, no. 37.

relationship and the generativity of their love through the gift of offspring. In sexual intercourse, there is an inseparable connection established by God between the unitive meaning and the procreative meaning, both of which are inherent to human sexual intercourse. Since not every act of sexual intercourse will result in a new life, spouses may use this knowledge to plan their family and to exercise their maternal and paternal responsibilities sensibly under the guidance of the Holy Spirit. This is their right and duty.[3]

REGULATION OF CONCEPTION

40. Health and social service organizations are encouraged to foster responsible parenthood and to promote the various methods of the regulation of conception that respect a woman's natural fertility cycles as well as her own health.

41. The use of procedures or drugs deliberately and intentionally to deprive the marital act of its procreative potential, whether temporarily or permanently, is morally unacceptable.

42. Educators and health professionals in relevant programs are to be well informed on natural family planning methods. They are to provide instruction honestly and objectively about these methods, so that couples can make free and informed decisions for responsible parenthood. (Refer to article 14.)

STERILIZATION

43. Direct sterilization, whether permanent or temporary, for a man or a woman, may not be used for the regulation of conception.

---

3. See "Pastoral Message of the Canadian Conference of Catholic Bishops on the Occasion of the 40th anniversary of the Encyclical *Humanae Vitae*," Sept. 26, 2008, nos. 14-16.

44. Procedures that induce sterility are permitted when their direct effect is the cure or alleviation of a present and serious pathology and a simpler treatment is not available.[4]

ACCEPTABLE MEANS TO AID FERTILIZATION

45. Means used to aid fertilization by the husband may be used appropriately within marriage as long as they facilitate the natural act of marital intercourse, thereby maintaining the unitive and procreative meanings of marriage.

UNACCEPTABLE MEANS TO AID FERTILIZATION

46. Artificial insemination by a donor (AID) i.e., insemination of a married woman with the sperm of a donor who is not her husband; fertilization with the husband's sperm of an ovum not from his wife; and any technology that causes a complete separation between procreation and the conjugal act are contrary to the dignity of the unity and covenant of marriage and should not be carried out in Catholic institutions.

47. *In vitro* fertilization (IVF) is not permitted because it separates procreation from the personal, sexual act of love of the couple. Moreover, it can lead to the deliberate destruction of embryos as well as to serious ethical, medical, psychological and social problems in multiple births, including selective abortion, and long-term complications for these children. This practice does not respect human dignity insofar as it tends to make embryos a commodity and tends to compromise the professional responsibility of those who enable such

4. See United States Conference of Catholic Bishops (USCCB), *Ethical and Religious Directives for Catholic Health Care Services*, 2009, no. 53. Also, Congregation for the Doctrine of the Faith, "Concerning 'Uterine Isolation' and Related Matters," 1993.

procedures. While IVF, even when done within marriage, "is not marked by all that ethical negativity found in extra-conjugal procreation," it is still illicit and cannot be performed in Catholic institutions.[5]

48. In all cases, children born from such procedures are to be treated with the same positive love and respect as any other children. (Refer to article 16.)

49. Fertilization using the sperm and/or ovum from a deceased spouse(s) violates the natural aspect of the conjugal act as well as the dignity of the child by deliberately separating the child from the bonding and nurturing normally coming from the biological parents.

REPRODUCTIVE SURROGACY

50. Since reproductive surrogacy ordinarily implies IVF and artificial insemination, it is not permitted because these procedures are not permitted. Moreover, it can lead to a consideration of the child as an object of contract and to the commercialization of human procreation. It also blurs the natural links between parent and child and puts the surrogate mother and the child into an unnecessary situation in which they will have to live the psychological consequences of a mutual abandonment. (Refer to articles 46, 47.)

RESPECT FOR EMBRYOS AND FETUSES

51. In the light of modern eugenic trends, it must be emphasized that all embryos or fetuses deserve the same respect owed

---

5. Congregation for the Doctrine of the Faith, *Donum Vitae (Gift of Life) – Instruction on Respect for Human Life in its Origin and on the Dignity of Procreation – Replies to Certain Questions of the Day*, Vatican, 1987, II, B, 5.

to any human being, no matter what anomaly they may carry.[6] (Refer to articles 57, 130-135.)

52. Direct abortion, i.e., any deliberate action where the purpose of the action is to deprive an embryo or a fetus of life, is never permitted. (Refer to articles 53-55.)

MEDICAL TREATMENT OF PREGNANT WOMEN

53. Medical treatment for a pregnant woman is permitted to prevent or cure a grave illness in the pregnant woman (e.g., premature rupture of membranes) that cannot be deferred until the unborn child is viable, even if it will result in the death of the unborn child.

54. Ectopic pregnancies constitute a major threat to the life of the mother and the embryo or fetus. While direct abortion is not permitted, current interventions aimed primarily at trying to resolve the pathological condition threatening the mother's life, even if they result in the death of the embryo or fetus, are morally justified. (Refer to article 52.)

EARLY INDUCTION AFTER VIABILITY

55. For a proportionate reason, labour may be induced after the fetus is viable.[7]

56. Prenatal diagnosis sometimes reveals a pregnancy involving a fetus with a lethal anomaly. In managing these pregnancies, the fetus and a possible premature birth must be treated with

6. See Pope John Paul II, Encyclical Letter *Evangelium Vitae* (*The Gospel of Life*), on the Value and Inviolability of Human Life, Vatican, 1995, no. 57.

7. United States Conference of Catholic Bishops (USCCB), *Ethical and Religious Directives for Catholic Health Care Services*, 2009, Directive 49.

the same unconditional respect that is due to a healthy child. In some of these situations, there may be life-threatening risks to the health of the mother from present or future complications. Also, the deteriorating condition of the fetus sometimes causes life-threatening risks to the mother as the pregnancy continues, making it medically and morally appropriate to induce delivery before full term. Therefore, for proportionate reasons, such inductions may be permitted after the fetus has reached presumed viability. However, clinicians should first consider practising proactive health management for the good of the mother and the child and be sensitive to those parents who want to take the child to term despite possible risks. The intention of any early induction must not be to cause the death of the child.[8] (Refer to articles 52, 55.)

CRYOPRESERVATION

57.   The freezing of embryos constitutes an offence against the respect due to human beings by exposing them to grave risks of death or harm to their physical integrity, and by depriving them, at least temporarily, of maternal shelter and gestation, thus placing them in a situation in which further offences and manipulation are possible. (Refer to articles 51, 130, 132, 134.)

---

8.   United States Conference of Catholic Bishops (USCCB), *Ethical and Religious Directives for Catholic Health Care Services*, 2009. Directives nos. 45, 47, 49. See also, Catholic Health Australia, *Code of Ethical Standards for Catholic Health and Aged Care Services in Australia*, 2001, no. 2.31.

CONDITIONS FOR PARTICIPATION IN GENETIC SCREENING PROGRAMS

58. Individuals may participate voluntarily in a genetic screening program for research, education or genetic counselling, as long as their informed consent is obtained and no disproportionate risks are involved. They must understand the consequences of testing and that there may be significant implications not only for themselves but also for other family members sharing genetic traits and for the future of their families. Such understanding is necessary for them to be able to make informed and morally correct decisions for any current treatment and for any subsequent treatment decisions. Confidentiality of data must be maintained, given the risk of discrimination or other inappropriate uses. (Refer to articles 17, 18, 21, 51, 59, 61.)

PRE-IMPLANTATION DIAGNOSIS

59. Pre-implantation diagnosis is often done to ensure that only embryos free from defects or having the desired sex or other specific qualities are transferred. Such qualitative selection and consequent destruction of embryos are an expression of a eugenic mentality, which works to prevent the birth of children with various kinds of anomalies. As well, it can be seen as legitimizing infanticide and euthanasia. Also, the human embryo may be considered as mere "laboratory material," subject to alteration and experimentation. Such use is an offense against human dignity and so must be considered as "immoral."[9] (Refer to articles 1, 18, 51, 58.)

PRENATAL DIAGNOSIS AND TREATMENT

60. Prenatal diagnostic procedures with the informed and free consent of the parents are permitted as long as they respect the life and integrity of the embryos and fetuses and are directed toward their protection or healing. The anticipated benefits for both the parents and the unborn must outweigh the risks involved in the diagnostic procedures. (Refer to articles 1, 18, 51, 58, 131.)

61. The presentation of any diagnostic information is to be complete and balanced, allowing adequate time for advice to make a morally good decision. It is to be communicated in a supportive manner with no attempt to link prenatal diagnosis to direct abortion. Supportive pastoral counselling that respects the dignity of every human life is to be made available for the parents. (Refer to articles 17, 18, 24, 58.)

CARE OF PARENTS, FAMILY MEMBERS AND STAFF IN DISTRESS

62. Compassionate care and support, including perinatal palliative care, are to be provided to parents of children born with severe malformations or disabilities, to those who lose a child through a miscarriage (sometimes referred to as spontaneous abortion) or stillbirth, and to family members and staff. Every effort should be made to provide the Sacrament of Baptism for live births, according to the religious sensibilities of the parents. (Refer to article 24.)

---

9. Ibid., no. 22.

63. Catholic health and social service organizations are to provide compassionate physical, psychological, emotional and spiritual care for those women and men who are distressed due to their involvement in abortions. (Refer to article 24.)

CARE OF HUMAN REMAINS

64. A policy should be in place to ensure that all aborted embryos and fetuses, and the remains of miscarriages and stillbirths, are buried or cremated in a respectful manner and in an appropriate place. (Refer to articles 25, 107.)

Chapter Four

Care at the End of Life

Introductory Comments

Sickness, suffering and dying are an inevitable part of human experience and are a reminder of the limits of human existence. Rooted in charity, Catholic health and social services are called to respect the dignity of persons, to foster trust and to promote justice. This chapter focuses on these three calls as they affect care issues at the end of life. The Catholic tradition faces the reality of suffering and death with the confidence of faith. In the face of death, the Church witnesses to her belief that God has created each person for eternal life. Suffering and death are not a final end but rather a passage transformed by the promise of the resurrection.

As a witness to this faith and to the call to provide care as Jesus did, Catholic health care facilities are to be communities of respect, love, and support to those receiving care and to their families, whatever their cultural and religious beliefs, as they face the reality of debilitating chronic illness and death. One of the primary goals of health care for the dying is to relieve pain and suffering. Effective management of pain in all its forms is critical in the appropriate care of the sick and dying, whatever their age or circumstances.

The experience of facing death can be a time of deep self-awareness and not merely an inevitable process to which persons must passively submit. It can be a time in which persons freely and consciously affirm the meaning of their lives. It can also be an occasion of profound reconciliation with family and friends, though all of these possible responses depend on the concrete situation and cultural and religious background of the person facing death. For that reason, spiritual and religious care are essential elements of care for those who are facing death. Catholic health and social service organizations, along with local parish communities, should be responsive to the needs of dying persons and their families.

Life-threatening illness and death in infancy and childhood bring unique ethical and pastoral challenges. Parents are generally, and rightly, the primary decision makers for their children. Clinical and pastoral support is given to them as they make difficult and often tragic decisions in their child's best interest. Awareness of and response to the parents' and family's attachment and grief, regardless of the length of the child's life, are essential. Sensitivity to the significance of parental decisions to forgo or withdraw non-beneficial and burdensome interventions as death becomes inevitable are essential elements of compassionate care. As children mature, they should be respectfully involved in decisions regarding their health and health care. This is particularly important for children and adolescents with chronic, life-threatening illness.

Health and social service organizations are to provide education and special training to those who care for dying persons, especially because of enduring societal denial of and discomfort with death. The Catholic tradition holds that we are stewards but not the owners of our lives and, hence, do not have absolute power over life. We have a duty to preserve our life and to use it for the glory of God, but this life is not our final goal and so we recognize that the duty to preserve life is not absolute. Thus we may reject life-prolonging procedures that are insufficiently beneficial or excessively burdensome, though suicide and euthanasia are never morally acceptable options.[1] Health and social service organizations and parish communities should also offer programs on care of those who are dying, including advice on questions around advance care planning or living wills, organ and tissue donation, and pediatric palliative care.

Advances in science and technology are dramatically improving our ability to cure illness, ease suffering and prolong life. These advances also raise ethical questions concerning end-of-life care, particularly around life-sustaining treatment. Reflection on the inherent dignity of human life and on the purpose and limits of medical treatment is indispensable for formulating a true moral judgement about the use of technology to maintain life. The use of life-sustaining technology is judged by Christians in the light of their understanding of the meaning of life, suffering and death. In this way, two extremes are avoided: on the one hand, an insistence on the provision of technology that cannot bring about the goal desired or that is considered overly burdensome by the person receiving care and, on the other hand, the forgoing of technology with the intention of causing death.[2] Because differences arise in judging what is possible and what is burdensome, it is crucial to ensure an atmosphere and processes in which differences can be attended to with mutual respect for the different knowledge and perspectives of all involved.

Good palliative care, that is, health care that aims to relieve suffering and improve the quality of living and dying, should be a key goal of all facilities that care for those nearing death.

1. Congregation for the Doctrine of the Faith, *Declaration on Euthanasia*, Vatican, 1980. See also United States Conference of Catholic Bishops (USCCB), *Ethical and Religious Directives for Catholic Health Care Services*, 2009, Part Five: Introduction.

2. Congregation for the Doctrine of the Faith, *Declaration on Euthanasia*, Vatican, 1980.

> The human person is to be respected through every stage of life. In caring for persons at the end of life, Catholic organizations should be responsive to the needs of sick and dying persons and their families.

CARE OF PERSONS AT THE END OF LIFE

65. Dying persons are to be provided with care, compassion and comfort. This should include the following: appropriate health care; pain and symptom management; social, emotional, spiritual and religious support; full information about their condition, as culturally appropriate; the opportunity for discussion with health care personnel; full disclosure to any family member or other person authorized by the dying person to receive this information; and a degree of privacy that ensures death with dignity and peace. For Catholics, this means providing for the Sacraments of Reconciliation, Anointing of the Sick, as well as Viaticum (communion). (Refer to articles 16-23, 66, 77-79.)

66. Some diseases, especially certain infectious diseases with fatal outcomes, or diseases that stigmatize, place special demands on care providers and require concerted efforts in education and prevention. Individuals with such diseases deserve the same standards of care as other persons receiving care; they are to be treated with compassion and respect. (Refer to articles 12, 16.)

PALLIATIVE CARE

67. The physical, emotional, psychological and spiritual care that characterizes palliative care should be available to all who have a life-limiting illness. It should be provided in all health care settings, including the home. Health care and social service providers, along with parish communities, are encouraged to be actively involved in securing palliative care for those persons and families in need of it. (Refer to articles 6, 7, 9, 24, 25.)

68. A person receiving care should be given sufficient pain and symptom management, by health care professionals who are knowledgeable in pain and symptom management, to lessen pain and suffering. It is important to note that these medications, if used appropriately, are effective, safe and do not hasten death. The goal is to alleviate pain and suffering while minimizing the potential side effects of medication. Such treatment does not constitute euthanasia but rather good pain management.[3] Persons experiencing pain and other symptoms should be cared for by health professionals with training in this area, to ensure that they have the competencies required to use these medications appropriately.

69. Palliative sedation can be morally permissible within the Catholic tradition. Patients should be kept as free of pain as possible so that they may die comfortably. Since a person has the right to prepare for his or her death while fully conscious, he or she should not be deprived of consciousness without a compelling reason. However, situations may occur when pain, shortness

---

3. Congregation for the Doctrine of the Faith, *Declaration on Euthanasia*, Part III, Vatican, 1980.

of breath or other symptoms cannot be alleviated without interfering with consciousness. Medicines capable of alleviating or suppressing symptoms in such situations may be given to a dying person. While these medicines show no evidence of shortening life if used in the last days, this therapy would be morally acceptable even if this therapy might indirectly shorten the person's life, so long as the intent is not to hasten death.[4] Hospital staff must do their best to make certain that the patient has had the opportunity to prepare for death and deal with spiritual, familial, social and other concerns before loss of consciousness becomes medically necessary. For Catholic patients, this includes the opportunity for the Sacraments. (Refer to articles 77-79, 85.)

DECISION MAKING AND THE DYING PERSON

70. In making decisions about the treatment of the dying person, the wishes, values and beliefs of the person receiving care should be the primary consideration. As much as reasonably possible, treatment decisions should reflect an agreement among those involved in the care of the person, including, as appropriate, family members and those who are significant in the person's life. (Refer to articles 17, 18, 22, 23.)

71. When a person with an underlying fatal pathology is capable of making his or her own decisions, the person should be given sufficient information concerning his or her medical status, the degree of uncertainty involved, the potentially life-sustaining treatments that are available, alternative plans of care and the probable consequences of each. Choosing a

---

4. See United States Conference of Catholic Bishops (USCCB), *Ethical and Religious Directives for Catholic Health Care Services*, 2009, Directive 61.

care plan on the basis of this information is often a difficult and time-consuming process. Care providers are called to take time to discuss and help the patient choose an alternative that best meets the patient's goals, that respects the patient's informed decisions, and that does not contradict Catholic teaching. Such decision-making processes should also take into account unique cultural and religious circumstances, where possible. (Refer to articles 16-18, 25, 78.)

72. When a person is not capable of making his or her own decisions with respect to treatment, every effort is to be made to ensure that the choice of health care treatment is consistent with the person's known wishes, values and beliefs, as long as these do not contradict Catholic teaching. Hence, treatment choices made by the person's surrogate should be based on the dying person's previously expressed directives, wishes, values and beliefs or, if these are not known, on overall best interests. (Refer to articles 19, 20, 90, 91.)

73. When decisions are being made for infants and children who have not yet achieved decisional maturity, the parents or authorized surrogates will use the standard of the best interests of the child. As children mature, they should be respectfully involved in the decisions. (Refer to articles 74-76, 93.)

74. Decisions about end-of-life care often require weighing the benefits and burdens of treatment options for the person receiving care. Such decisions should take into account the person's expressed wishes; his or her physical and emotional condition, including excessive pain, suffering, expense or other serious inconvenience; as well as the person's culture, religion, personal goals, relationships, values and beliefs. (Refer to articles 1, 18, 20, 25, 71.)

75. Decisions about end-of-life care are not concerned only with the person receiving care; the concerns of caregivers and the community should also be considered.[5] (Refer to articles 1, 4, 17, 20, 77, 89.)

76. Persons who are capable of making treatment decisions or their surrogates should seek those treatments that offer a reasonable hope of benefit and that can be obtained and used without excessive pain, expense or other serious inconvenience. (Refer to articles 1, 20, 77.)

REFUSING AND STOPPING TREATMENT

77. Persons receiving care are not obligated to seek treatment that will not accomplish the goal for which the treatment is intended or when the burdens (excessive pain, expense or other serious inconvenience) resulting from treatment are clearly disproportionate to the benefits hoped for or obtained. (Refer to articles 1, 20, 76.)

78. Even when life-sustaining treatment has been undertaken, this treatment may be withdrawn, with consent of the person receiving care or the person's surrogate, when there is no longer a reasonable hope of benefit or when the burdens outweigh the benefits as judged by the person receiving care or by their surrogate. (Refer to articles 17, 18, 20, 70-76, 90, 91.)

79. A decision to forgo life-sustaining treatment must not mean abandonment of the person receiving care. Palliative care, which is treatment, should always be provided and, the dignity of the person always respected. The person's comfort, as

---

5. Congregation for the Doctrine of the Faith, *Declaration on Euthanasia*, Part IV, Vatican, 1980.

well as social, emotional, psychological and spiritual support, must be maintained. (Refer to articles 24, 67, 69.)

ATTENDING TO DIFFERENCES AND DISTRESS IN DECISION MAKING

80. End-of-life decisions are ideally made by the capable person receiving care in consultation with the care providers, family and those who are significant in the person's life. Differences in judgement may occur regarding what treatment goals are attainable, worthwhile or burdensome. (Refer to articles 17, 22, 23, 65.)

81. Health care professionals should propose as potential treatment options those that offer a reasonable hope of benefit, while recognizing the variability of what a patient might consider beneficial and the uncertainty of clinical judgement. Health care professionals are under no obligation to provide treatment that will not accomplish the goal for which it is intended, that is in conflict with Catholic moral teaching, or that would violate the health worker's conscience. If a health care professional determines that a particular treatment that might generally be expected will not be offered, the reasons for this decision need to be fully communicated to the patient or surrogate. (Refer to articles 17-20, 26.)

82. When differences arise regarding the appropriate treatment plan for the patient, health care professionals should attempt to engage the patient or surrogate to determine a treatment plan that is mutually agreed upon. Sometimes persons receiving care need time, patience and support to discern the appropriate decision. To aid this process, health care

professionals may wish to engage the services of an ethics consultation service, patient advocate, social worker, chaplain or other support service. Organizations caring for patients at the end of life should develop strategies and supports that foster meaningful communication and mutual understanding. If differences cannot be resolved and a mutually agreeable treatment plan determined, such differences may need to be referred to external bodies such as administrative tribunals or courts for resolution. (Refer to articles 158-163.)

MEDICALLY ASSISTED NUTRITION AND HYDRATION

83. Medically assisted or artificially provided nutrition and hydration raise issues related to such fundamental human realities as basic nourishment, mutual interdependence, and faithfulness to those who are vulnerable and dependent. Medically assisted nutrition and hydration require special training and serious attention to the human and ethical issues involved.

84. In principle, there is an obligation to provide patients with food and water, including medically assisted nutrition and hydration for those who cannot take food orally. This obligation extends to patients in chronic and presumably irreversible conditions who can reasonably be expected to live indefinitely if given such care. Medically assisted nutrition and hydration become morally optional when they cannot reasonably be expected to prolong life or when they would be "excessively burdensome for the patient or [would] cause significant physical discomfort, for example resulting from complications in the use of the means employed."[6] For instance, as a patient draws close to inevitable death from an underlying progressive

and fatal condition, certain measures to provide nutrition and hydration may become excessively burdensome and therefore not obligatory in light of their very limited ability to prolong life or provide comfort.[7] The criteria on which to base any decision to withhold or discontinue medically assisted nutrition or hydration are to respect the needs, values and wishes of the person receiving care.[8] The intent must never be to hasten death. (Refer to articles 20, 71, 74, 78, 87, 89.)

85. Since some pathological conditions experienced by those who are dying prevent normal food ingestion, a decision to forgo or stop medically assisted nutrition and hydration can allow the pathology to run its course without prolonging the dying process. Such a decision is not the same as "hastening death."[9] (Refer to articles 67-69, 89.)

CARDIOPULMONARY RESUSCITATION

86. Cardiopulmonary resuscitation (CPR) is an aggressive treatment used in situations of unexpected cardiac arrest. When deciding about CPR or about orders not to attempt resuscitation, both the potential benefits and burdens should be duly considered and patients should be encouraged to discuss this treatment with their health care providers.

---

6. Pope John Paul II, Address to the Participants in the International Congress on "Life-Sustaining Treatments and Vegetative State: Scientific Advances and Ethical Dilemmas" (March 20, 2004), no. 4.

7. United States Conference of Catholic Bishops (USCCB), *Ethical and Religious Directives for Catholic Health Care Services*, 2009, Directive 58.

8. Congregation for the Doctrine of the Faith, *Declaration on Euthanasia*, Part IV, Vatican, 1980.

9. Ibid.

However, it is not ordinarily indicated for use on persons who have reached the end stages of a progressive fatal condition. (Refer to articles 74, 89.)

SUICIDE AND EUTHANASIA

87. Treatment decisions for the person receiving care are never to include actions or omissions that intentionally cause death (euthanasia). (Refer to articles 20, 68, 85.)

88. Intentionally causing one's own death (suicide), or directly assisting in such an action (assisted suicide), is morally wrong. (Refer to article 89.)

89. Refusal by the person receiving care to begin or to continue to use a medical procedure in which the burdens, harm and risks of harm are out of proportion to any anticipated benefit is not the equivalent of suicide. It may be considered an acceptance of the human condition, a wish to avoid the application of a medical procedure that is disproportionate to the beneficial results that can be expected, or it may reflect an acceptable desire not to impose excessive burden on the family or community.[10] (Refer to articles 1, 4, 17, 20, 74, 75, 77.)

ADVANCE CARE PLANNING

90. Advance health care planning (e.g., advance directives, living will) enables a person to communicate their directions concerning the type of treatment they desire should they lose their ability to make decisions for themselves. Persons are encouraged to discuss these wishes with their family and

10. Ibid.

health care professionals and, if appropriate, to appoint a surrogate before crisis situations arise. A statement of values, beliefs and potential treatment goals, when included as part of a written advance health care plan, assists family and care providers to carry out the wishes of the person receiving care. (Refer to articles 17, 19, 20, 72, 74, 78.)

91. A person's written or oral health care preferences are to be respected and followed when those directions do not conflict with the mission and values of the organization. Advance directives or living wills, which seek to clarify issues surrounding end-of-life treatment, are to be discussed and carried out in a compassionate and sensitive manner. (Refer to articles 17, 19, 20, 72, 74, 76, 79.)

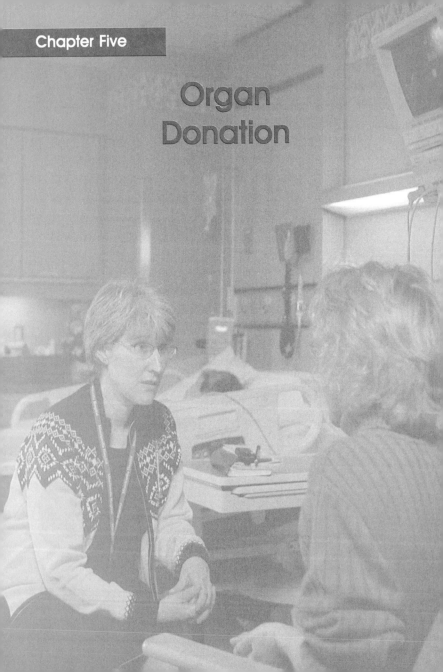

Chapter Five

Organ Donation

Introductory Comments

Rooted in charity, Catholic health and social services are called to respect the dignity of persons, to foster trust and to promote justice. This chapter focuses particularly on solidarity and on issues of respect for human dignity in regard to organ donation. People live and grow as beings interconnected with other members of the human community. Advances in medicine have made organ, blood and other tissue transplants a way to improve health and to give new life to countless people. Organ and tissue donation is an expression of respect for the dignity of persons, solidarity with other members of the human community, and charity in response to the needs and suffering of others.

From a Christian perspective, as members of the human community, we are co-creators and stewards of God's creation. We are to use our gifts to benefit ourselves, other individuals and the common good. In honouring the sacredness of every human life, Christians are encouraged to be generous in their response to God's call to love through the self-giving that comes from volunteering to be an organ donor.[1]

In applying its ethical principles to the issue of organ and tissue donation and transplantation, the Church teaches that transplanting organs and tissues from a dead person to a living person, and transplanting organs and tissues from one living person to another, are ethically acceptable, provided that the following criteria are met: there is a serious need on the part of the recipient that cannot usually be fulfilled in any other way; the functional integrity of the

---

1. Pope John Paul II, Encyclical Letter *Evangelium Vitae* (*The Gospel of Life*) On the Value and Inviolability of Human Life, Vatican, 1995, no. 86.

living donor as a human person is not impaired; the risk taken by the living donor as an act of charity is proportionate to the good resulting for the recipient; the donor's and the recipient's consent are free and informed. Any transplant that would replace a person's personal or procreative identity with that of another is contrary to the human dignity of the person. The desirability and perceived necessity of organ transplantation must not override the respect owed to living, dying and even deceased persons and should take into account the demands of justice.

Many Catholic health care organizations provide a vital link in the donation and transplantation of organs and tissues. They have a responsibility to provide this service with respect. Health care professionals are ideally suited for promoting organ donation and for educating the public about the subject.

Schools, parishes and community organizations should highlight the merits of organ and tissue donation and transplantation. Such activities would help to bring this issue into people's homes and encourage them to express their wishes to family and care providers.

Participation in organ and tissue donation and transplantation is understood as an expression of solidarity, charity and respect for human dignity. In the donation and transplantation of human organs, the functional integrity of the living donors involved is to be maintained.

RESPECT FOR DONOR AND RECIPIENT

92. In the donation and transplantation of human organs and tissues, respect is to be given to the donor and to the recipient. In any transplantation, whether from another or from oneself,[2] the functional integrity of the living donor concerned is always to be maintained. The free and informed consent of both donor and recipient must be ensured. (Refer to articles 16-19.)

93. Special care is to be given in circumstances in which minors are recipients of organ donation, particularly when parents or siblings are donors. Recognizing the natural sense of parental duty to the welfare of their children, care must be given to avoid coercion or undue influence on parents to donate. Organ or tissue donation by minors or others lacking decision-making capacity may be permitted in rare circumstances. (Refer to articles 73, 92, 96.)

94. Any use of human tissue (e.g., placentas, cell lines) without full disclosure of potential uses and the informed consent of the person from whom the tissue is obtained is contrary to respect for the dignity of persons. (Refer to articles 16-18.)

ELIGIBILITY FOR BEING A RECIPIENT

95. The choice of transplant recipients should reflect the equality of all people and should not be based on criteria of personal or social worth. The recipients of organs are to be chosen according to principles of distributive justice, with emphasis on maximizing the impact of the donation on the quality and quantity of life and recognizing and respecting the donated

---

2. See *allogeneic* and *autologous* in the Glossary.

tissues and organs as limited and precious gifts. (Refer to articles 1, 12, 16, 152.)

LIVING DONORS

96. The transplantation of an organ from one person to another is justified only if the good to be derived by the recipient is in proportion to the foreseeable risk to the donor. This requires that donors not be deprived of life or of the integrity of their bodily functions, that the transplanted organ be donated without coercion, and that the donor's consent or that of the donor's surrogate be free and informed. (Refer to articles 17-19.)

DECEASED DONORS

97. The retrieval of organs from deceased individuals is permissible when it is based on the donor's previously expressed wish. In the absence of the donor's previously expressed wishes, authorization for organ donation from the deceased person's legal representative is required. Any previously expressed objections of the deceased should be respected. (Refer to articles 90, 91.)

98. Care providers are to ensure that the compassionate care available to any dying person is provided to a dying patient who is a potential donor. No removal of organs or other invasive activity for the purpose of organ or tissue donation may begin until the death of the donor has been determined in accord with medical and legal requirements. Those making the determination of death ought not be related to a transplant program or to any person likely to become a recipient of organs or tissues provided by the donor. (Refer to the definition "Death" in the Glossary, and to articles 100-102.)

99. The decision to use pre-mortem medications for the sake of preserving or enhancing potentially viable organs is permissible only if specifically agreed to on the basis of full, informed and voluntary consent. Nevertheless, the use of pre-mortem medications or interventions should be offered only when there is no significant risk of harm or of hastening death.

DONATION AFTER CARDIAC DEATH

100. There are two sets of medical criteria for determining death: cardio-respiratory criteria and neurological criteria. Both sets of criteria can be used to determine the irretrievable loss of all integrated brain functioning, which is generally agreed to be the basic criterion that underlies the biological concept of human death. Thus, determination of death by cardio-respiratory criteria requires not only the absence of circulation, but also its biological permanence (not simply the absence of intention to resuscitate) and sufficient time without circulation to allow for the irretrievable loss of all integrated brain functioning. (Refer to article 98.)

101. It is possible to allow for the donation of organs or tissues from a deceased donor after declaration of death by either set of criteria (cardio-respiratory or neurological). Donation after determination of death by cardio-respiratory criteria requires careful attention to the requirements noted in article 100 above in order to reflect respect both for the gift and for the life of the donor.

102. At the present time, there is uncertainty about the minimal period of time following cessation of circulation that is required to determine the permanent loss of circulation and the irretrievable loss of all integrated brain functioning. In

light of this current uncertainty, communities and organizations involved in organ donation should establish guidelines, policies or procedures that offer direction in this area based on the best evidence available at the time. In all cases, including those in which death is both imminent and inevitable, respect for life, recognition of the dignity of the potential donor and avoidance of any tendency to hasten death should guide decisions right up to the time of death.[3]

DISTINCT HEALTH CARE AND TRANSPLANTATION TEAMS

103. The team providing care to the donor should not overlap with members of the transplant team so that potential conflict of interest may be avoided. (Refer to article 98.)

MONETARY REMUNERATION

104. Monetary remuneration for tissue or organ donations contradicts the principle of charity or altruism which is part of the necessary justification for such transplantations. Organs, blood and other tissues, therefore, must not be bought or sold as commodities. However, compensation for health care or other costs incurred by the donor or donor's family can be provided. (Refer to article 11.)

---

3. At the present time, there is sufficient moral certainty that, in people who already have severe brain injury with evidence of brainstem impairment, 10 minutes of absent circulation will result in irretrievable loss of integrated brainstem function and therefore satisfy the criteria for determination of death. Nevertheless, some argue that 5 minutes, or even 2 minutes, is sufficient. Until evidence is more certain, a prudential judgement concerning this matter will continue to be required. See also Canadian Catholic Bioethics Institute, *Organ Donation: A Catholic Perspective*, 2009. Published as a policy document for the Archdiocese of Toronto.

DONATION FROM ABORTED FETUSES

105. Transplantations using organs and tissues from deliberately aborted fetuses are ethically objectionable insofar as this practice may legitimate abortions. No human life is ever to be conceived or used simply as a means to obtain tissues or organs for transplant purposes.

BRAIN CELL TRANSPLANTATIONS

106. Transplantations to the brain in order to restore functions lost through disease are permitted if the personal identity and abilities of the recipient are not essentially compromised.

DISPOSAL OF HUMAN ORGANS AND TISSUES

107. The dignity of the human person requires that human organs and tissues be treated with respect. They are not to be considered as simply pathological or biomedical waste. Institutions must develop a protocol for their proper disposal. The faith traditions and cultural practices of the persons involved are to be respected. (Refer to articles 25, 64.)

USE OF ANIMALS

108. Transplantation of animal cells, tissues or organs into humans (xenotransplantation) is increasingly viewed as one possibility for overcoming human organ shortages. However, such transplantations might transmit an infectious agent to a recipient and, in turn, to others. Such risks, together with the ethical implications, should be clearly understood and consented to by recipients and others involved. Those who wish to undertake xenotransplantation have the burden to show that the procedure is both safe and ethical. (Refer to article 13.)

109. The use of animal parts for transplantations, such as replacement heart valves from pigs, is permissible as long as these can fulfill an essentially beneficial function in the recipient and the recipient is fully informed as to the nature of the animal biological material to ensure that there are no cultural or religious objections. (Refer to articles 17, 18, 25.)

110. In the case of xenotransplantation, animals being prepared as sources for transplantable organs or tissues are to be treated with the care required from the stewards of God's creation. (Refer to article 140.)

Chapter Six

Research Involving Humans

Introductory Comments

Rooted in charity, Catholic health and social services are called to respect the dignity of persons, to foster trust and to promote justice. This chapter focuses on issues of respect for human life and dignity, of solidarity and of justice in regard to research involving humans.

Research involving humans continues to increase in breadth and intensity and provides significant benefits for the human community. New knowledge and understanding in health care, the social sciences and technology help alleviate human suffering, improve treatments for illnesses and enhance health status. The findings of research involving human participants[1] can offer creative solutions and hope for individuals, for particular groups and for society as a whole. The participation of individuals in research studies, as investigators or as participants, is an affirmation of solidarity with others. The manner in which research is carried out must always respect the dignity and integrity of the persons involved and must serve the common good.

The Catholic tradition encourages us to participate in research as a way of being in solidarity with others.[2] As co-creators with God,

---

1. There has been significant discussion in Canada over the past twenty years regarding the appropriate term to describe those on, or about whom, research is carried out, that is, whether to use the term "participant" or "subject." The current standard in Canada, which will be used in this *Health Ethics Guide*, is to use the term "participant." See *Tri-Council Policy Statement: Ethical Conduct for Research Involving Humans*, 2010, *TCPS2* Article 2.1 discussion.

2. Congregation for the Doctrine of the Faith, *Donum Vitae (Gift of Life) Instruction on Respect for Human Life in its Origin and on the Dignity of Procreation – Replies to Certain Questions of the Day*, Vatican, 1987, Introduction, no.2.

we are to use our gifts of intelligence and freedom to enhance our understanding of all aspects of human life, and to develop health care and social services, including medical technologies, methodologies and basic sciences that will benefit the human community.

Catholic health and social service organizations, as well as educational institutions engaged in research involving human participants, have a responsibility to communicate and foster a respectful ethical attitude toward such research.

In the field of health care, research is expanding beyond the goal of trying to find better drugs or other treatments for disease. Research-like methodology is being applied more and more to processes of health care delivery in a way that often makes it difficult to distinguish studies that are seen to be research from studies that are considered to be evaluation, quality assurance or quality improvement. This chapter of the *Health Ethics Guide* speaks specifically to issues of research strictly defined. However, the same basic principles should be applied to other kinds of studies.

The comments here provide a brief outline of the Christian perspective on the value of human research and its goal of serving the common good. This chapter does not attempt to duplicate the extensive work already done regarding the ethics of human research. Rather, it seeks first to highlight and endorse some now generally acknowledged values and principles described in many documents regarding the ethical conduct of research involving humans,[3] and secondly to speak to some specific values and principles of the Catholic tradition that relate to research.[4]

> Research must always respect and safeguard the life, dignity and integrity of the persons involved. It should respect the communities involved and be directed to the benefit of the human community as a whole.

PURPOSE OF RESEARCH

111. The purpose or goal of research involving humans is to contribute to the advancement of knowledge and the welfare of the community.

CRITERIA FOR RESEARCH STUDIES

112. The knowledge sought through research with human participants must be important and obtainable by no other

---

3. Among the many documents are included the World Medical Association's *Declaration of Helsinki* (1964 to current 2008 versions), the *Belmont Report* (1979), the International Council on Harmonization: *Good Clinical Practice Guidelines*, and specifically in Canada, the *Tri-Council Policy Statement: Ethical Conduct for Research Involving Humans*, 2010, TCPS2 along with various provincial laws and regulations, particularly around health care decision making, privacy and protection of personal health information.

4. Recent authoritative teachings reflecting the Catholic tradition include, among others:

   • Pope John Paul II, Encyclical Letter *Evangelium Vitae (The Gospel of Life)*, Instruction on the Value and Inviolability of Human Life, Vatican, 1995, no. 86.

   • Congregation for the Doctrine of the Faith, *Donum Vitae (Gift of Life) Instruction on Respect for Human Life in its Origin and on the Dignity of Procreation – Replies to Certain Questions of the Day*, Vatican, 1987.

   • Congregation for the Doctrine of the Faith, *Dignitas Personae* (*Dignity of the Person*), Instruction on Certain Bioethical Questions, Vatican, 2008.

means; those carrying out the research must be qualified; and the methodology used must be scientifically sound.

113. The foreseeable harms to participants in research must not outweigh potential benefits.

114. Research with human participants requires free and informed consent from the appropriate decision maker. (Refer to articles 18, 19, 123-125.)

115. Respect for the dignity of persons entails special obligations toward those who are marginalized and those who may be vulnerable in the context of research, such as children and individuals who are institutionalized, or those in dependent situations or other situations that may compromise voluntariness of consent. Such individuals or groups may be particularly vulnerable to abuse, exploitation or discrimination and may require special procedures to protect their interests. (Refer to article 12.)

116. Respect for community as well as for individuals requires that research within Aboriginal communities abide by the particular requirements of those communities regarding the goals and conduct of the research. (Refer to article 25.)

117. Justice requires that no part of the population be exploited or be unfairly burdened with the harms of research, and that no groups be discriminated against through exclusion from participation in research or in receiving benefits from advances in research.

118. Thus, justice requires that women ought not to be automatically excluded from research solely on the basis of sex or reproductive capacity. Such exclusions may deny potential benefits of research to women and may expose

women to an increased risk of harm from the use of treatments studied only in men. Nevertheless, inclusion of women in research, especially pregnant or breastfeeding women, must take into account and make clear the possible risks of the research not only to the woman, but also to any actual or potential pregnancy or developing child.

119. Appropriate review of research ought to be conducted by a Research Ethics Board that is constituted and operates according to recognized standards and guidelines. The more ethically challenging the research, the more stringent should be the review.

120. Researchers have a duty to publicly disseminate the analysis and interpretation of any significant findings. Silence concerning negative research results may foster potentially harmful health care practices, other interventions or wasteful duplication.

121. Respect for persons requires that researchers respect the privacy of individuals and maintain confidentiality of information they have obtained regarding research participants. (Refer to article 21.)

122. Research conducted by or in Catholic organizations must be consistent with the values outlined in this *Health Ethics Guide*. (Refer to article 15.)

CONSENT, CAPACITY AND INFORMED DECISION MAKING

123. Research involving human participants who are capable of making their own decisions may only proceed with their free and informed consent. The requirement to secure consent from potential research participants is rooted ethically, and

legally, in the principle of respect for the dignity of persons. Consent for participation in research involves more than completion of paperwork related to a study.

The goal of the consent process is to ensure that the prospective participant is making a free, informed and voluntary decision regarding participation or non-participation in any proposed research. Researchers should ensure especially that participants are aware that, even after initial agreement, they have a right to withdraw from a study at any time or for any reason. (Refer to articles 18, 114.)

124. Prospective research participants should receive written information about the research in which they are being asked to participate and, typically, sign a written informed consent form. Those who decline to participate in research, or those who agree to be research participants but later choose to withdraw from the research, must be assured as part of the consent process that their health care will not be affected by their decision.

125. In principle, persons who lack decision-making capacity should not be excluded as research participants simply because of their incapacity. However, such persons may be included as research participants only with appropriate third party authorization, taking into consideration any expressed wishes or beliefs of the potential research participant. Researchers should pay particular attention to legal considerations and requirements when contemplating the enrolment of persons who lack decision-making capacity in research studies. Those who have impaired decision-making capacity or who lack decision-making capacity are especially vulnerable and should not be enrolled in research that is unrelated to their particular

health and social circumstances. If persons lacking decision-making capacity are to be included in research, they should be exposed to no more than minimal risk in the research except where there is potential direct benefit for them. (Refer to articles 19, 90, 91, 117.)

PROTECTION OF PERSONAL HEALTH INFORMATION

126. Respect for the dignity of persons requires that we honour and protect the privacy and confidentiality of patients, clients, residents and research participants. In a therapeutic relationship, it is understood that a number of direct care providers may legitimately access personal health information as part of providing care. In the research context, however, it is expected that researchers will secure the consent of patients/clients prior to accessing any personal health information for research purposes. In some jurisdictions, there may be exceptions to this consent requirement. Research Ethics Boards may, in particular circumstances, waive this requirement. Researchers should be aware of relevant provincial privacy legislation and, where appropriate or required, federal legislation. (Refer to article 21.)

127. Organizations that oversee personal health information or researchers entrusted with the collection and storage of data, information and biological specimens must pay particular attention to maintaining the privacy, confidentiality and security of the data. (Refer to article 21.)

CONFLICT OF INTEREST

128. A conflict of interest or the appearance of a conflict of interest occurs when an individual or institution in a position of trust has competing interests that may interfere with the fulfillment

of existing ethical and legal obligations and commitments. Competing interests almost always relate to a personal or corporate benefit. A growing reliance on private, for-profit organizations for research funding has increased the likelihood that some researchers, health care facilities or universities will find themselves in a conflict of interest in the course of carrying out research.

129. Researchers should disclose real or perceived conflicts of interest to the organizations where the research is to be carried out. In addition, Research Ethics Boards should be advised of any real or perceived conflicts of interest, and this information should form part of the review of a research protocol. Researchers should also disclose the same to prospective research participants as part of the informed consent or decision-making process. (Refer to articles 177-179.)

RESEARCH ON GAMETES, EMBRYOS AND FETUSES

130. Research on embryos and fetuses, whether viable or not, must respect them as human beings. Manipulations of embryos and fetuses, whether proven or novel, are permitted only if the manipulations are intended to be therapeutic for these embryos and fetuses. (Refer to articles 51, 60.)

131. Therapeutic interventions on live embryos and fetuses may only be carried out when there is a reasonable expectation of benefit with no disproportionate harm to the life or integrity of the unborn child and the mother, and if the appropriate consent has been obtained. (Refer to articles 60, 130.)

132. Researchers must not produce, acquire or use living human embryos for a scientific, commercial or other purpose because

these practices treat a human subject as an object. (Refer to articles 51, 57.)

133. Any attempt to combine a human gamete with that of an animal is ethically unacceptable because it undermines the dignity of human beings.[5]

STEM CELL RESEARCH

134. Stem cell research holds promise of correcting numerous disease situations. There are various sources reported from which stem cells may be derived (e.g., human embryos, human umbilical cord and a growing list of adult cell types). Research on stem cells that are derived from sources that do not involve the destruction of a living human embryo is permissible. However, research using human embryonic stem cells is prohibited because it always involves the destruction of a living human embryo. (Refer to articles 51, 52.)

REPRODUCTIVE CLONING

135. Any attempt at the cloning of persons (usually called reproductive cloning) violates the fundamental integrity of what it means to be a person, treating both the person from whom the clone would be derived and a person resulting from the cloning as objects. It would be an act of domination, the imposition of one's particular genome on another being, fixing it forever, which would be a radical affront to the person's dignity, autonomy and freedom.[6]

---

5. Congregation for the Doctrine of the Faith, Instruction *Dignitas Personae* – (*Dignity of the Person*) on Certain Bioethical Questions, Vatican, 2008, no. 33.

GENETIC RESEARCH

136. Genetic research looks to understand the root causes of disease and to understand the mechanisms involved. It has as a goal the development of methods of diagnosis, prediction, prevention and treatment of disease. Genetic research impacts not only individuals, but also their related familial and ethnic groups. Since such research holds the potential for additional social and psychological harm, along with stigmatization and discrimination, researchers must be especially respectful of privacy, confidentiality and the social consequences of the information to which they are given access. (Refer to articles 18-21.)

137. Attempts to influence genetic inheritance that are aimed at the selection of human beings according to predetermined categories, such as gender, intelligence or physical ability, are manipulations contrary to the personal dignity, integrity and identity of the human being.

138. Interventions involving the introduction of genetic material into living human beings for the purpose of gene therapy may offer promise but must always be represented accurately. However, interventions that change the germ cell line are not permissible.

GENE PATENTING

139. As an essential element of the human body, the human genome should be regarded as the communal property of human society and not the property of a few.[7] While researchers should be

---

6. Ibid., nos. 28-29.

7. John Paul II, "Address to the Pontifical Academy of Sciences," October 1994.

able to patent the intellectual processes used in their research, the patenting of human genes, human cell lines and other human genetic materials poses serious ethical questions that should be carefully weighed. Such concerns include:

- the increased risk of dehumanizing and exploiting human persons;
- limitation of access to products created from patented human materials;
- the further commercialization of research;
- the risk of using genetic material from persons without their informed consent.

RESEARCH ON ANIMALS

140. Research on animals is often required before testing new therapies in human participants. Animals should be used in research only if necessary. Such research should show proper respect for the animals used, adhering to guidelines set up for that purpose.[8] When research on animals is justified, pain and distress must be minimized and proper pain relief provided. (Refer to article 110.)

---

8. The Canadian Council on Animal Care (www.ccac.ca/) provides comprehensive guidelines on the ethical use of animals and should be consulted.

Chapter Seven

Governance and Administration

Introductory Comments

Catholic health and social service organizations are communities of service, united through collaborative activities and inspired by Catholic moral principles. As visible expressions of the ministry of Christ, these tangible human institutions are organized, governed and administered for the purpose of providing an optimum level of care for those who are sick or in need, and promoting a healthy society and environment. At the same time, they are occupational communities providing for personnel a means of personal and professional fulfillment and a means of earning a living.

To meet these obligations, Catholic health and social service organizations are required to be identified in a tangible way as visible expressions of the ministry of Christ. This involves dimensions such as Catholic sponsorship and management; recognition by the local bishop of such organizations as an integral part of the apostolic activities of the local church; quality care; proper stewardship of resources for the community served; a culture that supports Catholic ethical values and spiritual beliefs; promotion of spiritual/religious care; mission and values integration; just working conditions; the availability of the sacraments and the presence of various Christian symbols. Moreover, the organization is called upon to act as a moral community by making ethical decisions related to governance and administration, and by striving for effective communication and consultation with all members of the organization and with the local bishop.

As a community of service that receives funds from the public to carry out its mission, the organization acts to meet obligations that correspond to its several roles:

- as an agency commissioned to provide services to the public;
- as a human community of service expressing solidarity with those in need of care;
- as a Christian community acting as a careful steward of God's gifts;
- as a Catholic organization accountable for governance and administrative practices congruent with its mission; and
- as a Church community committed to a preferential option for those who are poor and marginalized.

A Catholic organization cooperates appropriately with the diocesan bishop, who has the teaching responsibility of ensuring that the ethical and social teachings of the Church are reflected faithfully in the health and social service apostolate and who has the pastoral responsibility of providing for and overseeing sacramental ministry to Catholics receiving care in such organizations. Consultation and cooperation with the bishop are needed for him to fulfill his mandate to guarantee the Catholicity of the health or social service organization.

A Catholic health or social service organization must acknowledge that work is a dimension of a person's creativity, for it provides a community and a sense of meaning and purpose. As a community of work, the organization seeks to create an atmosphere within which work is viewed as more than an economic function, but also where personnel can use their gifts to flourish and grow, impact positive change in the health of the community, and enhance the mission of the organization in keeping with a quality work life for all concerned.

Board and senior administration should be guided by the vision of Catholic health care, as well as by professional, organizational, social and personal values. Selection and recruitment practices should maintain value alignment with the organization's mission and values, particularly its Catholic identity. Decisions made in or on behalf of an organization are ultimately organizational decisions and not personal ones. This should be reflected in all governance, employee and clinician practices and decision making.

As communities of service, Catholic health and social service organizations are dedicated to providing an optimum level of care for persons and to promoting the common good. As specifically Catholic health and social service organizations, they are identified in a tangible way as a visible expression of the ministry of Christ. As occupational communities, these organizations provide for employees an atmosphere for personal and professional fulfillment and a means of earning a living. In meeting such obligations, these organizations are informed by a moral vision and recognize the need to address the ethical dimension of decisions related to governance and administration.

GOVERNANCE

141. The governance structure for any organization designated as Catholic should state how the organization is related to the bishop and to the Holy See through its sponsor. This relationship should consider issues of oversight, endorsement

and the role of certain reserved powers[1] so that the organization will exercise appropriate responsibility for advancing itself as a visible expression of the ministry of Christ within the Church.

142. The selection of board members should also ensure that membership is representative of the different communities and cultures served by the organization. The mission of the organization is based on a worldview that flows from the Gospel and that reflects a respect for the dignity of persons and the sanctity of life as found in the Catholic tradition. Once selected and appointed, the sponsor and board members are responsible for articulating that mission. Ongoing education regarding the responsibilities of board members for maintaining the mission and Catholic identity of the organization should be a regular part of board meetings and retreats. (Refer to article 7.)

143. In accord with this core mission, board members and senior management are responsible for fostering a culture of hospitality and service, welcoming all who enter the facility with particular sensitivity to the needs of the persons they serve. This requires respect and compassion for those receiving care, or their families and for those providing care, while also seeking to be effective and efficient within the constraints imposed by limited resources. (Refer to articles 8-10, 151, 152.)

---

1. Powers that are "reserved" to the sponsor may include, for example, the following: approve any changes in the philosophy or mission of the organization; appoint and/or dismiss the board of directors; appoint the chair of the board; participate in the selection of the CEO; merge or dissolve the organization; appoint the auditor; amend the act of incorporation and the bylaws.

144. Board members and senior administration also have the responsibility of promoting the integration of the mission and the values of the organization, and of developing leadership throughout the entire organization. Responsible stewardship requires that board members and senior administration ensure that all board decisions are ethical ones. This includes financial considerations, just wages and treatment of personnel, planning and priority setting, and policy development. Those chosen to serve as board members should appreciate the importance of this ethical dimension of governance. (Refer to articles 156-160.)

145. While sharing certain responsibilities with senior management, the board has certain primary fiduciary obligations, including: setting board policy and the vision for the organization; selection, compensation and performance evaluation of the Chief Executive Officer; ensuring awareness and education around the history and legacy of the organization; governance and monitoring of board effectiveness; financial oversight and risk management; approval of physician credentialling, advocacy and mission fidelity; and quality of service.

146. The board's fiduciary responsibility for ensuring the quality and effectiveness of the health and social services provided entails setting policy to monitor, review and set targets for quality-of-care standards. In health care organizations, board-established Quality Assurance Committees, which may be protected under provincial legislation, provide an additional mechanism to investigate quality issues and to deepen ethical reflection in promoting a culture of discovery and learning to advance the overall quality of patient care. Research Ethics Boards or similar research ethics review committees may

also be accountable to the board in some organizations to monitor the types of research activities and the ways in which research is conducted. Ultimately, the mission of the organization is measured by both the quality of care and the compassionate attitude and approach with which it is provided. Mission is both quality *and* compassion. (Refer to articles 9, 10, 184.)

147. The recognized advocacy role of the board also provides an effective tool to promote its organizational values and influence the delivery of health and social services within related regional systems, government, associations and interest groups. Board policy should direct the advocacy agenda to further the mission, vision and strategic goals of the organization. (Refer to articles 9, 12.)

ADMINISTRATION

148. The administration coordinates the multiple functions of the organization in a way that encourages personnel and those receiving care to form a community of hospitality and service. This community is evidenced by organizational practices and behaviours that are service oriented, grounded in a Catholic vision that promotes justice, the common good, respect for varying cultures and traditions and a preferential option for the poor. The hallmark of the Catholic health or social service organization is how widely known it is for recruiting and retaining personnel who share this vision, and for nurturing growth of the vision and mission in those recruited. Those receiving care are also partners in forming this community of compassion through their participation in the decisions that affect them. (Refer to articles 8-10.)

149. In congruence with the organization's mission and values, administrative decision making and planning and policy formation should be participative processes, involving input from managers, health and social service professionals, other staff and representatives of the community served. (Refer to articles 8, 9, 160.)

COLLABORATIVE RELATIONSHIPS

150. Circumstances sometimes dictate that Catholic organizations enter into a variety of collaborative arrangements to minimize duplication of services, ensure quality and adequately respond to the range of community needs. This may include partnerships, alliances, joint ventures, as well as consolidated merger arrangements. The resulting collaborative relationships, which may be voluntary or mandated by civil authorities as part of a regional context, and organized to provide a continuum of integrated programs and services, bring both opportunities and risks. In developing and entering into such collaborative arrangements the following guidelines should be attended to:

- the mission and values of Catholic organizations are to be affirmed and protected;

- the board, governance and administrative structures should ensure effective promotion of the organization's mission and values;

- the principle of cooperation, applied analogously to matters of moral decision making at the organizational level, should form the ethical context for such partnerships. (Refer to Appendix I.)

- local bishops and other Church authorities should be kept informed of the development of collaborative arrangements relating to matters of faith and morals, which should not be completed without the authorization of the diocesan bishop.[2]

ALLOCATION OF RESOURCES

151. The careful stewardship of resources should be guided by the mission and values of the organization and with consideration of the common good. Resource allocation will often require a balancing between individual and communal needs, and should be applied fairly and equitably against a set of objective, organizational values-based criteria, while protecting the organization from financial risk. This can be best fostered within communities dedicated to dialogue, interdependence and concern.

Catholic organizations fulfill their responsibilities concerning resource allocation in a variety of ways, such as:

- active participation in the formulation of federal, provincial and local policy directions for the equitable distribution of funds;

- cooperation with other organizations to make limited resources available to more people;

- planning and distributing funds appropriately among programs and services within the organization;

- active concern for the special needs of the most disadvantaged among those receiving care and those in

---

2. United States Conference of Catholic Bishops (USCCB), *Ethical and Religious Directives for Catholic Health Care Services*, 2009, Directive 68.

the larger community within the context and obligations of a publicly funded system. (Refer to articles 9, 12, 16, 27, 28, 31, 144.)

152. Basic health care needs are not to be overlooked when allocating resources for procedures or programs involving expensive, scarce medical services. Concern and advocacy for the common good, while balancing the need for effective health promotion and disease prevention strategies, places limits on what resources can or should be allocated. For example, use of very expensive experimental drugs for a few individuals may prohibit obtaining an adequate supply of less costly proven drugs or therapies that could benefit more people, and the health of the community. (Refer to articles 1, 4, 5, 16, 95.)

RATIONING OF RESOURCES

153. When the resources available for health care and for social services are not sufficient to meet the needs of those seeking care, those who have the responsibility for rationing these limited resources are to consider the ethical dimension of any decisions to deny services or to select some individuals over others for services. Organizations must develop a suitable, transparent and equitably applied protocol to address the rationing of resources. Where standards of care might be impacted during a protracted crisis, such as an influenza pandemic, the reasons for the need to ration resources and to adjust triage criteria must be objective, transparent, publicly defensible and ethically justifiable. (Refer to articles 12, 16, 151, 158.)

SPIRITUAL AND RELIGIOUS CARE

154. Spiritual and religious care is provided in a variety of settings: within institutions, in the community, in parishes and at home. Such care includes pastoral visiting, counselling, in-service education, spiritual direction, individual and group prayer, and opportunities for celebrating the Sacraments and other religious rites. This care is important in all situations of illness and loss; it is essential in the context of end-of-life care. (Refer to articles 2, 6, 7, 10, 24, 25, 62, 63, 65.)

155. The appointment of priests and deacons to the spiritual care staff of a Catholic institution must have the explicit approval or confirmation of the local bishop in collaboration with the administration of the organization.[3] Catholic organizations should cooperate with the bishop in his responsibility for the spiritual and sacramental life of Catholics within the Catholic health care or social service institution in question. Wherever possible, these institutions should have a chapel for prayer and the regular celebration of the Mass.

FOSTERING AN ETHICAL ENVIRONMENT

156. There is an ethical dimension to all health care and social service decisions. Such an ethical environment is characterized in part by respectful and honest communication and by clear accountability around alignment of behaviour, clinical practices and operational decision making with the mission and values of the organization. It is important that resources be available to promote sound ethical decision making by all persons in the

---

3. *Cf.* United States Conference of Catholic Bishops (USCCB), *Ethical and Religious Directives for Catholic Health Care Services*, 2009, Directive 21.

organization. This responsibility is frequently facilitated by an ethics committee or by an ethics consultant or team. As more services are offered in the community, ethical resources will be required at the local and diocesan/parish level to assist those providing care, as well as those receiving care and their families, in the discernment of ethical issues. (Refer to articles 82, 144, 160, 162.)

157. Where ethics committees are established, an interdisciplinary membership is recommended. In order to ensure a collaborative approach to ethical reflection, a well-balanced ethics committee in a health care organization would include such representation as nurses, physicians, social workers, other health professionals, spiritual/religious care providers, ethicists, moral theologians, administrators, legal consultants and representatives of persons receiving care. There should be appropriate competency standards for ethics consultants and for ethics committee members. Those providing ethics consultation should be committed to Catholic moral teaching and should be familiar with this *Health Ethics Guide*. Standards for medical ethical consultation should respect the local bishop's teaching and pastoral responsibilities.[4]

158. The ethics consultant or committee may advise on particular ethical situations, promote education on ethical issues and, where appropriate, review and recommend organizational policies. They may also be a resource to assist in evaluating systemic issues from the perspective of social justice, and, if necessary, support the board in its advocacy role. (Refer to articles 12, 82.)

---

4. Ibid, Directive 37.

159. Procedures are to be established to address situations in which there is a need, but inadequate time, for ethics consultation. Such situations should be reviewed later by an ethics committee or consultation service to provide a retrospective review. (Refer to article 163.)

ESTABLISHING A PROCESS FOR ETHICAL REFLECTION BY MANAGEMENT

160. Organizations should encourage a forum for those with management responsibilities to reflect on the ethical dimension of their work. (Refer to articles 146, 148, 149.)

161. The ultimate goal of all ethical reflection by management, and indeed by all those involved in these ethical processes, is to bring the healing, compassion and reconciliation of Jesus to all who form the health and social service communities. (Refer to article 10.)

ADDRESSING ETHICAL ISSUES

162. Each organization is to set up a resolution process to address ethical uncertainty or differences that arise among health professionals, persons receiving care, and/or the organization. The mission, values and Catholic identity of the organization should provide the defining framework in clarifying justifiable options and recommendations. (Refer to articles 82, 163, 164.)

163. Situations arise in which recommended care options are also limited by the organization because of human or financial resources. If a health care professional is of the opinion that a patient is not being offered a particular treatment that should reasonably be provided, the health care provider should

advocate for their patient. However, a health care provider may not use shared resources that are beyond their discretion to use. Organizations need to balance the individual needs of particular patients with the reasonable needs of the community and the common good. Compassion, human dignity, stewardship and justice should guide such decisions. A review or appeals process should be put into place to promote fairness and transparency. (Refer to articles 1, 151-153, 156-159.)

164. Care providers often play multiple roles and express multiple loyalties in the same situation. For example, care providers might be called upon to be both patient advocate and gatekeeper to services. Efforts should be made to reduce the occasions in which providers must serve conflicting roles. The education of all care providers should address the ethical conflicts that can arise in serving in such conflicting roles. (Refer to articles 156-159.)

ORGANIZATIONAL RESPONSE TO CONSCIENTIOUS OBJECTION

165. No one may be required to participate in an activity that in conscience the person considers to be immoral. While continuing to fulfill its mission, the organization is to provide for and to facilitate the exercise of conscientious objection without threat of reprisals. However, the exercise of conscientious objection must not put the person receiving care at risk of harm or abandonment. This may require informing the person receiving care of other options for care. (Refer to articles 8, 17, 20, 26, 81, 163, 166, Appendix II.)

DUTY TO CARE

166. During emergency or mass casualty events such as a pandemic, health care workers have an obligation to provide care to others who depend on their special skills and training. These duties, which arise out of the call to compassion and to foster trust and solidarity, may need to be balanced with the competing duties of care that providers understandably have toward self, family and others. In order to mitigate competing obligations and conscientious objection to work obligations, health care organizations should provide appropriate training, appropriate personal protective equipment, a possibility of reassignment of staff to minimal risk areas, and other harm-reducing strategies in an effort to sustain the health care system during a protracted crisis. Policies and procedures must be enacted to avoid ever abandoning the persons receiving care.

    An ethics framework that fosters the moral integrity of staff, by balancing the duty to provide care and the duty to self, should be developed and communicated to staff in advance to help reduce the possibility of placing people in situations in which they must in conscience choose between competing obligations. (Refer to articles 1, 7, 156, 162, 165, 181.)

EMPLOYER/EMPLOYEE RELATIONSHIPS

167. All members of the organization are to respect and act in accordance with the organization's mission and values. The primary responsibility of everyone in the organization is the person receiving care. To enhance the mission and the care, employees should exercise respect for one another. (Refer to articles 8-10.)

168. The organization should treat personnel respectfully and justly. The employer/employee relationship calls for fairness and mutual accountability from both the organization (represented by the board and administration) and from those who work in the organization. Boards have a fiduciary responsibility to set policy governing employee/employer relations that uphold the values of the organization. (Refer to articles 10, 16.)

169. Those who give direct care and those whose work enables care providers to function effectively should be valued as carrying out different but important aspects of the mission and operation of the organization. All persons are to be treated with respect and equal consideration in employment practices. (Refer to articles 16, 25.)

170. The expertise and experienced judgement of care providers are to be acknowledged in their individual areas of competency. Similarly, teams of care providers should respect the diverse expertise of their members in providing consultation, making decisions and delivering services. (Refer to articles 68, 81, 82.)

171. Equal opportunity for employment and career development should be available to all, irrespective of gender, race, age, national origin, disability, or other differences, unless the differences interfere with the ability to fulfill the obligations of the office. All are entitled to fair compensation and benefits for their work. (Refer to articles 16, 25.)

172. The employer must recognize the right of employees to form associations to engage in collective bargaining, to provide various benefits for their members and to work for a better society. All members of the organization are to encourage a

collaborative approach between unions and administration based on the good of the person receiving care. Respectful dialogue and behaviour should govern grievance and other non-escalating conflict resolution processes, with priority given to the principle of subsidiarity in mediating differences at the most basic level.

173. In light of its commitment to respect individuals and its recognition of the value of involving all levels of staff in planning and decision making, organizations should develop explicit guidelines for situations in which it becomes necessary to lay off workers. This implies consultation with those affected, examination of alternatives, open communication, and a flexible approach to honour the uniqueness of each individual. Staff layoffs should be a last resort; one that is used only after all other alternatives have been seriously tried. Treatment of non-unionized employees should be as consistent as possible with that of unionized employees. Employees terminated as a result of downsizing or program changes should be treated equitably and with respect and compassion. Employees terminated with cause should be treated with compassion and respect.

174. Financial realities and other operational issues may result in the need to contract out some services to ensure the sustainability of the organization, and/or to ensure the highest standards of care. When contracting out work, care should be taken to ensure that all contracting out arrangements respect the rights and responsibilities of unions, provide just wages and benefits, do not treat work as a commodity, do not endanger the sense of community within the organization, and do not threaten the quality of work or the mission of the organization.

175. Succession planning and leadership formation opportunities should be continually pursued to develop and prepare the next generation of health and social service leaders for the Catholic organization.

176. Recruitment and retention practices should reflect a commitment to Catholic moral teaching and ethical practices. For example, employee referral and other inducement programs, or recruitment of internationally educated health and social service workers, should be carefully considered in light of the organization's mission and values, as well as of Catholic social teaching around solidarity and justice.

CONFLICT OF INTEREST

177. Pursuit of wealth by care providers should always be secondary to their primary responsibility to promote health and relieve suffering. (Refer to articles 128, 129.)

178. Referral of persons to organizations in which the referring professional has an investment interest is usually a conflict of interest and is therefore ethically inappropriate.

179. Where conflict of interest is unavoidable, it should nevertheless be transparently disclosed and appropriately managed. Policy and processes for declaring real or potential conflict of interest should be adhered to by board, senior executive and all those personnel responsible for vendor, purchasing and business contracts.

ALTERNATIVE SOURCES OF REVENUE

180. In seeking additional or supplemental sources of revenue, health and social service organizations are to establish

guidelines to ensure that such activities are undertaken in an ethical manner. This requires a strategy to mitigate harm to those participating in certain revenue-generating strategies that may disproportionately target the poor and vulnerable and potentially create further community harm (e.g., video lottery terminal revenues).

- In the direct solicitation of donations, policies should be developed that ensure there is no coercion and/or breach of patient/resident/client confidentiality.

- Funds received for specific purposes must be devoted to those goals.

- Financial investments are to be consistent with the mission and values of the organization. From time to time, this may require a mission or organizational ethics consult. (Refer to articles 8, 9, 11, 144, 151-153, 160.)

ABUSE OF CARE PROVIDERS

181. Health and social service organizations are to develop policies and guidelines that recognize the obligation to provide care in situations of risk, set limits concerning the level of care to be provided in such situations, and provide mechanisms for protecting the safety of care providers. (Refer to articles 166-168.)

182. The organization must make it clear that it will not tolerate violence and abuse toward care providers and should establish guidelines for addressing such situations. Care providers should receive training on how to deal with prejudicial attitudes and behaviours, while working actively to promote a more culturally sensitive workplace that respects the diversity of

both personnel and the persons receiving care. (Refer to article 146.)

DEALING WITH COMPLAINTS

183. Organizations should have a well publicized process for responding to complaints regarding personal or corporate misconduct. The process is to consider complaints received from both 1) those receiving care, their surrogates or family, and 2) employees or staff (including whistleblowing). This process should include:

- the naming of an office within the organization to receive and investigate complaints;
- mechanisms for assuring a prompt investigation;
- full opportunity for all parties to present their positions;
- protection from reprisals for the person reporting misconduct in good faith, and for witnesses; and
- a preventative strategy to promote corporate compliance and integrity by ensuring that a confidential reporting or "whistleblowing" process is developed.

DISCLOSURE OF ADVERSE EVENTS OR POSSIBLE SCANDAL

184. At all times, a culture of safety and discovery should be promoted, with a commitment to upholding the dignity and respect of all persons affected. Disclosure practices governing reporting of adverse events should be consistent with the mission and values of the organization and all regulatory and legislative practices. A root cause analysis

should be conducted to mitigate potential harm from occurring in the future, and appropriate steps should be taken to remain in dialogue with and to support the person receiving care and their family during the investigation. Moreover, any adverse event or similar issue related to Catholic identity or the moral integrity of the organization should be reported to the local bishop. (Refer to articles 8, 9, 10, 146.)

Appendices

APPENDIX I

Making Moral Judgements

Conscience

The *Health Ethics Guide* has adopted a model of conscience in which conscience is understood to be at the core of the human person and of human dignity. In the Judeo-Christian tradition, the notion of the dignity of the human person is closely tied to the notion of responsibility. Human persons are constituted in the image of God especially because they are responsible for the direction of their own lives and are responsible for the welfare of others.

Catholic theological tradition has analyzed the notion of responsibility in terms of two interconnected notions: free will and conscience. The human person is responsible insofar as they can choose freely and insofar as by conscience they knowingly direct their actions.

Conscience is the ability of the human person to judge what is a morally good or a morally evil way to act in a particular situation. The objective moral good in a particular situation is that course of action that brings persons toward their fullest human potential and to their ultimate end, which is God.

To make correct judgements of conscience, a person must possess correct general moral principles. Some moral principles spring immediately from the nature of human persons and from their elevated state as adopted children of God and do not admit of exceptions (e.g., "It is always wrong to intentionally kill an innocent human person."). Other moral principles are more particular formulations that may admit of exceptions when they come in conflict with other principles in a particular situation (see the "Interpretive Principles" below).

To make correct judgements of conscience, the person must also have an adequate knowledge of the facts of the particular situation, along with the virtue of prudence, which enables the person to correctly apply the general principles to the particular situation. The prudent person is skilled at identifying those moral principles and rules that apply to the concrete situation, and at discerning which of the possible alternatives most fully embodies the applicable principles. In cases of unavoidable conflict, the prudent person is skilled in discerning which rule takes precedence in the particular situation.

Moral principles are known by revelation, as embodied in Sacred Scripture, and by natural law, which is known by human reason apart from revelation. The Catholic moral tradition represents the accumulated wisdom of the Church and includes interpretation of the Sacred Scriptures, reflection on the Scriptures and human experience, and the testing of opinions by criticism and the exchange of theological argument. The Magisterium or teaching authority of the Church provides the authoritative interpretation of the moral law, based upon Sacred Scripture, natural law and tradition. In this way, the individual's conscience, with its limitations, avails itself of the accumulated wisdom of the wider community, which is the Church.

Interpretive Principles

In addition to the values outlined at the beginning of this *Health Ethics Guide* and to the moral principles described throughout the *Health Ethics Guide*, the Catholic moral tradition offers several other principles that aid in interpreting particular kinds of moral situations.

1. **Burden and benefit** – This principle states that we are not obliged to begin or continue treatments that offer no reasonable hope of benefit, or that may constitute a grave burden, excessive pain, suffering, expense or other serious inconvenience to the person or to those who are responsible for their care. The principle is often expressed in terms of treatment being ordinary/ extraordinary, proportionate/disproportionate, beneficial/ non-beneficial, etc.

2. **Double effect reasoning** – Some human actions have both a beneficial and a harmful result, e.g., some pain treatment for a terminally ill person might carry a possibility of shortening life, even though it is given to relieve pain and is not intended to kill the person.

    Five conditions are cited for trying to decide if such actions would be morally permissible:

    i.   The action of the person must be morally good or at least neutral in itself.

    ii.   There are two anticipated outcomes for the action of the person, one intended and good, the other an unintended but foreseen evil.

    iii. The evil effect is not the means to the good effect.

    iv.   There must be a proportionate reason to accept the evil effect.

    v.   There must be no less-negative alternative.

3. **Totality and integrity** – A part of the body may be
    sacrificed to save the whole. For example, an organ may
    be sacrificed if it is the only way to prevent the death of
    the person. The moral tradition of the Church provides
    safeguards to protect against causing unjustified harm.
    The principle of totality points to a safe exception to the
    principle that one may not cause harm. Because the
    good of the whole is greater than the good of the part, it
    is justifiable to sacrifice the part for the whole. The
    Catholic tradition has limited the application of this
    principle to cases where the only function of the part is
    to serve the whole. For example, the eye has no function
    apart from being part of a living body. The tradition does
    not allow the principle of totality to be applied
    indiscriminately when the part has a proper function
    apart from the whole, as is the case of persons, who
    besides serving the state of which they are a part also
    have a value as individuals.

4. **Subsidiarity** – Decisions and functions ought to be
    handled by the smallest, lowest or least centralized
    competent authority; that is, "a community of higher
    order should not interfere with the internal life of a
    community of a lower order, depriving the latter of its
    functions, but rather should support it in case of need
    and help to co-ordinate its activity with the activities of
    the rest of society, always with a view to the common
    good."[1] As applied to health care needs, the principle
    suggests that the first responsibility for meeting these

---

1. Pope John Paul II, *Centesimus Annus (On the Hundredth Anniversary of
    Rerum Novarum)*, Vatican, 1991, no. 48.

needs resides with the free and competent individual. Individuals, however, are not completely self-sufficient. Usually, they can achieve health and obtain health care only with the help of their family members, their caregivers and the community. The responsibility of fulfilling those needs that the individual cannot achieve alone must be assumed by larger or more complex groups, e.g., community organizations and different levels of government, without resorting to "micro-managing," which is contrary to the principle of subsidiarity.

5. **Principle of Cooperation** – It often happens that achieving certain good results may involve cooperating with others who are performing morally wrong actions.

    The Catholic moral tradition distinguishes formal from material cooperation in a morally wrong action. In formal cooperation one agrees with the wrong action. It constitutes one's purpose in acting, as when, for example, one willingly cooperates in a theft because one wishes to profit from the theft. In material cooperation, one cooperates with an action without agreeing with it.

    One is never permitted to cooperate formally in the evil action of another, because such cooperation involves intending that evil be done.

    Material cooperation admits of different degrees. In what we here call "immediate material cooperation," one's action is indistinguishable from that of the principal agent. Immediate material cooperation is permitted only in cases in which the good sought would justify the evil result, even if one were the sole principal agent, not cooperating with another. For example, one would be justified in immediate material cooperation in harming someone in a lesser way in order to save his or her life. However, "Catholic health care organizations are not permitted to engage in immediate material cooperation in actions that are intrinsically immoral, such as abortion, euthanasia, assisted suicide, and direct sterilization."[2]

In assessing other kinds of material cooperation, four factors must be considered:

i.   The greater the good that is sought or evil avoided, the more likely it is that the cooperation is permissible.

ii.   The greater the evil that is tolerated, the less likely it is that the cooperation is permissible.

iii.   The more remote the cooperation, the more likely it is that it is permitted.

iv.   If the good in question can be achieved in a way that avoids the evil produced by the cooperative act, the cooperation is to be avoided unless the alternative will cause a proportionate or greater evil.

In calculating evil results, one must take account not only of the evil intrinsic to the action but also of any scandal that is likely to result. When it is a question of policy or general practice rather than of isolated actions, then the more general effects of cooperation or non-cooperation

---

2. See United States Conference of Catholic Bishops (USCCB), *Ethical and Religious Directives for Catholic Health Care Services*, 2009, Directive 70.

must be considered. Among the good effects to be considered are the continuance of a Catholic health care facility and its service, not only to patients but to making the Church's influence present in a significant area of society. Among the evil effects to be considered are the possibility that a wrong practice will become entrenched and accepted or that public perception of the Church's teaching will become clouded and uncertain.

Questions of cooperation in morally objectionable actions are often very complex and difficult to resolve. In making decisions in matters of policy, it is important to consult widely among prudent and experienced experts. A policy or an agreement among institutions involving cooperation in morally questionable actions should not be accepted without the approval of those who are officially responsible for designating an institution as a Catholic institution – normally the local bishop.

APPENDIX II

Glossary of Terms

Abortifacient
Medication or device that induces an abortion.

Abortion
A direct abortion is a procedure whose deliberate purpose is to terminate the life of an embryo or a fetus whether before or after implantation. An indirect abortion is a procedure necessary to save the life of the mother in which the death of the fetus is an inevitable result, e.g., the removal of a cancerous uterus during pregnancy.

Advance health care directives (Living will)
A document for instructing or informing others concerning a person's needs, values, wishes, the identity of the proxy and/or the type of treatment a person desires should they lose their decision-making capacity or be unable to make their wishes known.

AID
Artificial insemination by a donor.

AIH
Artificial insemination by the husband.

Allocation
The designation or setting aside of resources for specific purposes. (*see also* Rationing)

Allogeneic transfer (Allograft)

The transfer of body organs or tissue, e.g., skin or bone, from one individual to another individual of the same species.

Anatomical integrity

see Bodily integrity

Artificial fertilization

see In vitro

Artificial insemination

see In vivo

Assisted suicide

Counselling, abetting or aiding someone to kill themselves.

Autologous transfer (Autograft)

The transfer of body organs or tissue, e.g., skin or bone, from one part to another part of the same individual.

Bioethics

That part of ethics that deals with issues of life in the context of the life and health sciences. This is a word first used by Van Rensselaer Potter in 1971. It is a combination of two Greek words, *bios* meaning "life" and *ethos* meaning "custom."

Bodily integrity (anatomical/functional)

"Anatomical integrity" refers to the presence of all the organs of a normal human body. "Functional integrity" refers to the systematic efficiency of the human body. For example, if one kidney were missing from a person's body, there would be a lack of anatomical integrity, but functional integrity would remain, since the person would still retain adequate renal function.

Brain death

see Death

Caregiver

Caregiver is a term that usually refers to those persons who comprise the wide circle of support for a person in need of care, e.g., family members, a life partner, close friends or members of the broader community. It is sometimes used more broadly to also include care providers (see below).

Care provider

Care provider refers to someone who offers health or social services in a professional or paid capacity within a health or social service organization.

Capacitation (Sperm capacitation)

The chemical changes in sperm that occur in the female genital tract and that increase the sperm's capacity to penetrate and fertilize an ovum.

Cloning

In the context of this document, cloning is the production of an organism that is a genetic copy of the organism from which it was derived, done through processes such as transplantation or fusion of a nucleus of a source cell to an egg that will allow for further development.

Common good

The sum total of social conditions that allow people, either as groups or as individuals, to reach their fulfillment more fully and more easily (*Catechism of the Catholic Church*, no. 1906). It is sometimes referred to as the "common goal."

Confidentiality

A quality of human communication that protects a person's right to privacy by fostering trust between the care provider and the person receiving care. Confidentiality excludes unauthorized persons from gaining access to personal health information concerning the person receiving care, and requires that people who have such information refrain from communicating it to others.

Conscience

The specifically human capacity to judge what is morally good or morally evil behaviour in a particular situation. (For a fuller discussion refer to Appendix I.)

Conscientious objection

The refusal to perform an action based on moral or religious grounds.

Consent (informed)

Informed consent requires that an individual possess the capacity and freedom, as well as the understanding and appreciation of the information needed, to make a reasonable decision in their own best interests.

Contraception

The introduction of any means specifically intended to prevent conception from occurring as a result of sexual intercourse.

Cooperation (material)

Cooperating either immediately or remotely with a morally objectionable action of another. (*see also* Appendix I)

Cryopreservation

In the context of this guide, cryopreservation refers to the freezing of gametes and embryos in order to preserve them.

Death

With respect to the biomedical definition of death, persons are dead when they have irreversibly lost all ability to integrate and coordinate the physical and mental functions of the body. In regard to a precise time of death, death occurs: a) when the spontaneous functions of the heart and breathing have definitively ceased, or b) with "brain death," i.e., the irreversible arrest of all brain activity. In reality, the definitive arrest of cardiorespiratory activity very quickly leads to brain death. (Refer to *Charter for Health Care Workers*, Vatican, 1995, no. 129.)

Decision-making capacity

The ability of a person to make their own health care decisions. It is normally considered to include the ability to understand the information involved and to appreciate the consequences of a decision, the ability to reason from information to conclusions in light of a personal set of values, and the ability to express a choice.

Dignity of the human person

The inherent worth of the human person that calls for the deepest respect.

Distributive justice

The obligation of society to distribute the goods of that society equitably to its individual members.

Dysphoria

An emotional state of abnormal depression, anxiety and discontent.

Ectopic pregnancy

see Extrauterine pregnancy

Embryo (human)

The unborn child from the time of fertilization until the end of the eighth week of pregnancy.

Ethics

The study of the moral rightness or wrongness of human choice and behaviour; a set of principles of right conduct; reflection on values.

Euthanasia

An action or an omission that of itself and by intention causes death, in order that all suffering may in this way be eliminated. (*Evangelium Vitae*, no. 65)

Experimentation (Human)

Any research on human beings that seeks to verify or meaure the effect of a given treatment, e.g., pharmacological, teratogenic, surgical, etc. (*see also* Research).

Extrauterine pregnancy

A pregnancy in which the fertilized ovum implants somewhere other than in the uterus, e.g., in a fallopian tube or in the abdomen.

Fetus (human)

The developing child in the uterus from the end of the eighth week of pregnancy until the time of birth.

Functional integrity

see Bodily integrity

Guidelines

Criteria that guide or direct action.

Homograft

The transfer of human tissue or organs from one human being to another.

Human dignity
  see Dignity of the human person

Illicit
  Contrary to the law (divine, ecclesiastical or civil).

***In vitro* fertilization**
  The technique whereby an ovum or egg is fertilized by sperm in a petri dish ("in glass" – Latin) outside the body of the mother.

***In vivo* fertilization**
  A technique whereby an ovum is fertilized, not from sexual intercourse, but as a result of sperm being artificially introduced into the woman ("in a living being" – Latin).

IUD
  Intra-uterine device. This is a small device, usually made of plastic and containing copper or hormones, that is inserted into the uterus. It is most commonly used as a contraceptive device, but may also be used to treat certain medical problems.

Licit
  According to the law (divine, ecclesiastical or civil).

Living will
  see Advance health care directives

Ministry
  The specific manner in which the mission to heal is carried out in Christian health and social service organizations. This service is designated as ministry because it is motivated by the Gospel and is part of the Church's faith tradition.

Morality

This term has a number of meanings: that free human activity that perfects or fulfills a person's progress toward their ultimate destiny or detracts from it; the judgements of a person's conscience; the choices made and the objective elements of the human act; a system of norms or principles of good conduct for individuals or groups.

Moral certainty

A high degree of certainty that justifies action when absolute certainty is not available.

Palliative care

Palliative care, as a philosophy of care, is the combination of active and compassionate therapies intended to comfort individuals and their support communities who are facing the reality of impending death. It strives to meet physical, social, and spiritual expectations and needs, while remaining sensitive to personal, cultural and religious values, beliefs and practices. Palliative care is not limited to the end of life when a person has only days, weeks or months to live. Persons with progressive incurable illnesses may benefit from palliation of symptoms and other problems much earlier in their illness trajectory, even when they are receiving treatments such as chemotherapy to control their illness.

Palliative sedation

Palliative sedation therapy is the use of sedative medications to sedate, either lightly or deeply, a person who is experiencing intractable symptoms such as shortness of breath, confusion or pain when all regular methods have failed or are not possible. Research shows that palliative sedation therapy does not invariably shorten life.

Person

A being endowed with powers of intelligence and free will and the potential for moral consciousness and self-fulfillment in relationship to God and others. The individual remains a person, even if for some reason the potential is not actualized.

Personnel

In the context of this guide, personnel refers to all those who serve patients/residents/clients within health and social service organizations (e.g., administrators, physicians, nurses, other health and social service professionals, staff and volunteers).

Principle

A more specific articulation of a value that is used as a starting point or rule of thumb for good ethical reflection and action.

Protocol

The rules or formalities of any procedure or group.

Proxy

see Surrogate decision maker

Rationing

The withholding of potentially beneficial services because circumstances, policies and/or practices establish limits on the resources available for health care or social services. This definition is used because it clearly identifies what is of ethical concern (that is, the potential harm that can come from the denial of services) and recognizes that the practices or proposals to ration services must be tested against ethical criteria that assess the need for rationing, the methods proposed and their likely outcomes. *See* Allocation

Religion

The expression of spirituality through traditions, rites and practices usually within the context of an organized faith.

Research (clinical)

Any inductive-deductive process that aims at promoting the systematic observation and understanding of a given phenomenon in the human field or at verifying a hypothesis arising from previous observations. *(see also* Experimentation [Human])

Restraint

Any physical, environmental or chemical substance that controls a person's behaviour by preventing or restricting free physical movement.

Social justice

The concern to root out social habits, institutions, or structures that harm the common good of society, and to establish structures, ways of acting and attitudes, that promote the common good.

Sperm capacitation

see Capacitation

Spiritual and religious care

The activity of chaplains, community clergy, faith leaders and laity in helping persons to discover and deepen life and give expression to their spirituality and/or religion. In the context of Catholic health care, special emphasis is given to sacramental ministry.

Spirituality

The search for the sacred. A conscious striving to move beyond isolation and self-absorption to a deeper awareness of interconnectedness with the self, other human beings and the transcendent.

Stewardship
The exercise of responsibility in relationship to creation and the careful use of resources.

Substitute decision maker
see Surrogate decision maker

Surrogate decision maker
The person who is entitled to make care and treatment decisions for a person who lacks decision-making capacity. Alternative terms used include *proxy* and *substitute decision maker*.

Surrogate mother
A woman who allows a child to come to term in her womb with the understanding that she will turn the newborn infant over to the party or parties with whom she has made this arrangement or contract.

Therapeutic procedures
From a moral point of view, this usually refers to medical and surgical procedures that are related to the life-saving or healing interests of the person receiving care. (*see also* Research)

Transplant
The surgical operation of implanting a donated organ or tissue into a recipient, or the entire process from retrieval through to implantation.

Triage

The assignment of degrees of urgency to decide the order of treatment of those receiving care.

Value

That quality of the goodness of things that motivates human activity.

Xenotransplantation (xenogeneic/heterograft)

The transplantation from one species to another, e.g., animal to human. It is derived from the Greek *xenos* meaning "alien" or "stranger."

Zygote

The fertilized egg before it begins to divide into further cells.

INDEX

All references in the Index are directed to the page and not the number of the article.

E

F

G

R

X

Z